Face with a Heart

Mastering Authentic Beauty Makeup

Chris Scott

MAKEUP GOURMET

MeritusBooks
San Francisco

Face with a Heart
Mastering Authentic Beauty Makeup

By Chris Scott

Published 2014

ISBN 978-0-9707290-1-9

Cover design by Chris Scott and Diem Nguyen
Illustrations by Aile Hua
Makeup brush photos by Brian Long
Copy editor Susan Geye

About the cover

The cover design is an homage to Kevyn Aucoin who elegantly brought the beauty and power of makeup into our hands with his outstanding books.

About the author

CHRIS SCOTT, M.A. is the creator of San Francisco-based Makeup Gourmet®. Over his nearly 30-year career, in addition to doing makeup for top models from every corner of the planet, he also had the honor of working for legends like Paul McCartney, US Vice President Al Gore, Shirley Temple Black, Maya Angelou and Olympic Gold medalists Oksana Baiul and Kristi Yamaguchi. He was the creator and host of the TV show 'Makeup Gourmet' from 2008 – 2010. He was a leading Chanel Beauté national artist for over two decades, and is also the creator and guest teacher of Fashion Makeup at the Academy of Art University in San Francisco. He created his unique Makeup Gourmet line to ensure his clients and the public could have access to high-quality, ethically produced, 'green' makeup and skincare with a low-carbon footprint. Chris is also the author of the wonderfully visual 'how to' book Face with a Heart: Mastering Authentic Beauty Makeup (2014), as well as Cosmetic Counter Survival Guide: How to Buy the Right Skin Care and Makeup (2003).

Favorite saying that I think I made up:
The grass is always greener where you water it.

Please visit
www.MakeupGourmet.com

Contact
makeupgourmet@gmail.com

Dedication

I dedicate this book to every individual I have had the opportunity to apply makeup.
It is you who taught me how to honor each face, and how to keep the makeup true to you.

I also dedicate this book to Mary Jo who flies me like a kite.
Thank goodness for the string that connects us!

Table of Contents

Part One: Theory Behind the Technique

Part Two: How to Master Authentic Beauty Makeup

Dear Reader,

Face with a Heart is a breakthrough method of makeup application that works for all face types and lifestyles. Face with a Heart teaches both the theory and the practice of mastering true, authentic beauty makeup.

Creating a makeup application method that works for everyone and fulfills a client's expectations is a daunting task. As I have studied and practiced the art of beauty makeup, I have tried to answer these two questions: "What are universal beauty truths?" and "How do they translate from face to face?" The answers to these questions, coupled with the opportunity of applying makeup on over 50,000 clients in over 25 years helped me develop this method of makeup application. The criteria are always the same: find the most efficient way to create the absolute best results with each makeup application. The demands of this work forced me to clarify a method to handle the abundance of people I face each day.

When I became a fashion makeup instructor at the Academy of Art University in San Francisco, I started putting this method on paper so that I could better teach my students. You now hold in your hands the result of this work. Face with a Heart holds a double entendre: it is true to each person's authentic beauty and anatomy, and it celebrates the face as a physical centerpiece—a "highly structured grid"—that allows users of the method to intensify their individual beauty.

Equally appropriate for individuals and students of makeup alike, Face with a Heart method of makeup application redefines and demystifies how to achieve authentic beauty makeup. Authentic beauty makeup is the result of using the Face with a Heart method of makeup application and works in almost exact opposition to traditional beauty makeup. The direction of each brush stroke, order of application, well-defined borders, and simple color logic reinvents how makeup is applied and worn forever.

Traditional makeup is applied on top of the skin, and then spread out, eventually masking the face. Because the technique works by blending makeup down, product is being applied using a more-to-less (put it on-rub it in) method. The result reveals the makeup before the person wearing it; we see and become conscious of the makeup a person is wearing.

Through a markedly different approach to applying makeup, authentic makeup works in the opposite direction. It imperceptibly layers itself up away from the skin, creating an outward energy that reveals in precise detail, the features of the face. By layering makeup upwards and outwards from the skin, and only applying where and when you need it, the artist is in complete control of the desired intensity of the makeup. Authentic beauty makeup will always reveal the person before the makeup.

Once you read and incorporate these new techniques, you will master your makeup application, do it in a pleasing and efficient manner, and, most importantly, look and feel authentically beautiful every day.

With deep gratitude,

Chris Scott

How to use this book

This book is written for everyone who applies beauty makeup; valid for both self-application and to the makeup artist who applies makeup on someone else. When the term 'makeup artist' is used in this book, it refers to both self-application as well as those who apply makeup to others.

This book will speak strongly to technique so you can be the best makeup artist possible. No matter who sits in your chair (even if it's you!), you have the means and expertise to deliver a flawless, authentic beauty makeup application every time. Some faces are easier than others, and some faces wear makeup better than others. Your job as a makeup artist is to apply the best possible authentic makeup application to the anatomy of every person you encounter.

In order to achieve this level of confidence and skill mastery, this book will codify the anatomy of the face for you. It will break down into exact detail how and, more importantly, why you do the things you do. Rather than interpreting makeup application style from one face to another, you will have an exact anatomical formula that you will use, and it will adapt to the anatomy of every face to which you apply makeup.

Part one will instill in you the philosophy and theory of the Face with a Heart Authentic Beauty Makeup application. Part two will teach you how to do it, explaining everything you need to know so that you can master the application of Authentic Beauty Makeup.

Who is this book for? You!

PART ONE

Theory Behind The Technique

Beauty Makeup Vs Authentic Beauty Makeup

What is beauty makeup?

There is no question that makeup enhances how we appear to others. Understanding how makeup works its magic by creating such a profound effect is, in essence, beauty makeup. It is a term used to describe the style of makeup most widely applied by millions of people daily. It is part of the grooming process that creates how people want to look and how they want to be seen. Simply put, beauty makeup draws focus to the symmetry and balance of one's features while simultaneously distinguishing the communicators; eyes and lips.

The word beauty carries with it a certain amount of expectation. Not only are we to look better, we are to look beautiful, or so the word 'beauty' implies. While 'beauty' can be subjective, there are some core truths that create an authentic beauty look.

Face with a Heart will demonstrate how authentic beauty makeup applies those truths and will guide you in this process of application.

What is Authentic Beauty Makeup?

Authentic beauty makeup is part of the anatomy. Regardless of how natural or dramatic its effect, it is organically connected to the anatomy of the face. This effect is achieved by a series of techniques that always builds up and away from the structure and features of the face.

Although we wear clothes and jewelry on our bodies, the mindset for Face with a Heart is that we are not wearing makeup. Wearing makeup implies that it is something we have draped or attached to our body. This works for clothes and jewelry, but not for makeup. In short, makeup is part of our anatomy, not worn on or attached to our anatomy. Face with a Heart authentic beauty makeup appears to be born from and an extension of our actual skin.

AUTHENTIC BEAUTY MAKEUP

Authentic beauty makeup is in balance

Keys to makeup application: reduce the distractions and enhance the attractions. When applying makeup, the goal is for the sum of the makeup applied to equal 100%. If the artist uses the full force of their makeup in each step of the application, the makeup overpowers the features of the person wearing it. The makeup, not its effect, is noticed first. This is makeup out of balance.

The trick of achieving balance in your makeup application is to use just enough of everything. This dynamic will change from face to face, day to day, and from look to look. This is where artistry comes into play. Always be in the moment of the face you are working with, even if it is your own, and assess and apply the makeup as it is needed for the current application.

Use makeup where you need it, when you need it.

A study by David Leopold and Gillian Rhodes was done with primates on attraction. Primates were shown photographs of other primates with different degrees of symmetry and asymmetry in the features on the face. The more symmetrical and in balance the features were, the more the primates were interested in the photograph.

This is also true for human babies. In a study by Charles Feng, babies are seemingly calmed when the symmetry of the human face they are looking at is more in balance. Most people gravitate to balance and symmetry. For example, if a picture hanging on a wall is tilted, human instinct is to correct it by straightening it out.

When makeup is applied skillfully, it can create a greater sense of symmetry of the face. Symmetry equals balance and balance equals a peaceful grace.

Authentic beauty makeup is respectful.

A truly beautiful makeup carries with it a grace, a knowing, an ease with itself. It honors and celebrates the person to whom it is applied. It is not the makeup artist's position to decide what is beautiful; it is their job to honor and respect the face for whom they are applying makeup. In doing so, the true beauty of the makeup reveals itself and the person wearing it simultaneously.

The artist must learn to allow the face to dictate what it wants and needs, so they can become the conduit between the makeup product and the end result.

Authentic
beauty
makeup is
joyful.
The
best part of
applying beauty
makeup is the way it
makes the artist smile. Seeing
the effects of makeup artistry
as it lights up the face will
bring joy to the artist. Beautiful
makeup will always bring a
smile to the face of the
artist and his or her
client.

The Power of Makeup

Makeup has power because it affects how people see and feel about others. Makeup is also sensuous and personal and reflects how people see and feel about themselves. The vast array of products available today can create an endless combination of effects on people's faces. As a makeup artist, you want to be in control of these products and the effects they create, possessing the ability to conjure any image your mind may imagine.

As a makeup artist who respects both the client and the products he or she uses on the client, the variations and possibilities for success become limitless, The phrase: 'with great power comes great responsibility' may seem a bit deep for applying makeup. However, as a makeup artist, accepting and respecting the potential you hold with each application wields a magical powerful perception. To be known as someone who creates 'miracles' with their makeup work is to hold a great power and a great gift.

Be powerful with makeup by creating looks and finishes that stun and amaze your clients. The makeup applied should always stand alone and truly represent the concept of a Face with a Heart. For this, the makeup artist will be richly rewarded in status, respect and loyalty.

The Why? of Makeup

Knowing the why of makeup will greatly influence the how of makeup. A good question for makeup artists to constantly ask is 'Why'. Why contour? Why concealer? Why eye shadow? A makeup artist must know the reason for every decision made regarding product choice so that his or her makeup application becomes guided and meaningful. The sooner the makeup artist learns and embraces the 'Why', the more informed will become the 'How'.

Throughout this training manual, 'why', and not 'how', is the most important question to answer when applying makeup. Always ask 'why' first. Understanding the concept and purpose of Authentic Beauty Makeup before learning how to apply it is the key to success.

The 'how' of makeup is a learned set of skills and techniques a makeup artist calls upon when wanting to create precise effects. The 'why' of makeup is the essence, the spirit of the look that transforms the face and delivers a more authentic sense of beauty, not a generic look.

Each step of this training manual will teach every technique in two steps:

1. Why
2. How

This codified approach to beauty makeup is a system that is applicable to every face. It arranges the features of the face in such a simple, clear, and practical way that it standardizes the essence of authentic beauty makeup.

To teach this method of beauty makeup, it is mandatory that students bring no prior preconceptions of makeup to the learning process. When redefining the why and how of makeup at its very core and, at this level, there can be no other influence on the learning process.

The makeup artist visualizes a super-imposed heart-shaped grid on the client's face as they apply makeup. This allows the makeup artist to consistently achieve these makeup goals:

- Achieve absolute symmetry with any face
- Enhance to the fullest every feature of the face
- Achieve the desired balance between each feature

Authentic Beauty Makeup

LOOKS

Authentic beauty makeup manifests itself uniquely on everyone who wears it. Although over a billion people wear beauty makeup, all beauty makeup the makeup artist visualizes can be placed into one of the following groups.

Natural makeup

Not to be confused with no makeup. With natural makeup, the observer sees the person before their makeup

Balanced makeup

With balanced makeup, the observer sees the person at the same time as the makeup. In this instance, both the person's features and their makeup intensity are equal.

Dramatic makeup

With dramatic makeup, the observer sees the makeup before the person wearing it.

This may seem contradictory to the authentic makeup aesthetic, however it is not. As long as makeup is applied in accordance to this method by residing within the anatomy of the face, even the most dramatic makeup appears to be born from the skin. A vibrant red lip will always stand out. As long as it is applied authentically, it will celebrate the lips, not distort them.

Trend makeup

With trend makeup, one part of the makeup purposefully stands out from the others. The intention is that one particular aspect of the makeup is noticed before anything else on the face. Trend makeup is the most widely worn style of makeup, whether intentional or not.
Examples of trend makeup may include:

- Cat eyeliner
- Red Lips
- Highly blushed cheeks
- Super shiny skin
- Beauty mark
- Over emphasized brows
- Extreme glossy lips

All styles of makeup are represented within the authentic beauty makeup umbrella. The difference is how the makeup is applied to the anatomy of the face to achieve its authentic result.

These 'look' categories are designed to help the makeup artist control the effect created with each application and to critique the final result based on the original intention.

Put this classification system into another context. When ordering a steak, the question is 'How would you like that cooked?' The options are rare, medium-rare, medium, medium-well and well done. Each of these options carries with them a somewhat standard definition. It may vary slightly from cook to cook, but for the most part the definitions are understood.

This standard is far less defined in makeup. One person's natural is another person's dramatic. There is much more grey area when clients say they want a natural look as opposed to when they say they want their steak rare.

It is up to the makeup artist to define the intensity level of any makeup and to be able to communicate this with clients before starting the makeup application so there are fewer misunderstandings along the application process.

An easy observation lesson is to categorize everyone's makeup and learn to identify what differentiates one look from another. In doing so, the makeup artist will be better equipped to make these distinctions when applying makeup.

Look Book

Create a book of images of the different types of makeup that visually represents the different intensities of looks. This will easily solve communication between the makeup artist and his or her client (and yourself).

Your criteria for these images need to include:

- Face size needs to be at least half or more the size of the page. Small images leave out too much detail
- Be able to confidently categorize the look
- Make sure it is makeup you personally love
- Make sure it is makeup you can re-create or want to learn how to re-create
- Be able to breakdown/deconstruct the elements of the makeup to your client to explain why this makeup is effective

Use this Look Book with each client to determine what excites them. This tool is indispensable for clarity and clear communication between artist and model.

For makeup enthusiasts, this is a great learning tool to expand your skills when applying makeup to yourself. Many painters perfect their technique by copying painting styles they wish to emulate. The makeup enthusiast can also learn more about how to achieve the desired effects by 'figuring out' how a makeup is done from an image. Makeup artists also follow this discipline to become more proficient with their makeup application.

Most accomplished makeup artists have spent time recreating makeup looks they admire from print. As makeup styles are endless, the more looks that can be perfected, the deeper the pool of ideas to draw from when creating a fresh new look.

Color Intensity

The intensity of the makeup color is what defines whether a look is natural, balanced, or dramatic. Although the color selection process can be quite dynamic, there are some basic constants that keep your color intensity selection on track.
First observe the main existing color intensities of the model.

What to observe:
• Skin • Hair • Eyes (iris specifically)
Rather than define these features as colors, look at them as intensities.

The possibilities include:

- Light
- Medium-light
- Medium
- Medium-dark
- Dark

For a Natural look, have the darkest colors be no more intense than the darkest intensity of the model's features.

For a Balanced look, have the darkest colors equal to or just slightly darker than the darkest feature on the face.

For a Dramatic look, have the darkest colors significantly darker (or lighter if the features are predominantly dark already) than the features on the face.

By allowing the intensity of the color, rather than the amount of makeup, dictate the outcome of the look, it is possible to achieve a wide range of looks using the same amount of makeup.

This approach is key in achieving authentic beauty makeup where, regardless of the intensity of the makeup, the person is never concealed behind the makeup.

Structure of Face Shapes

A common question is "What is the shape of my face"?

Faces come in a wide variety of shapes, sizes and colors. It is easy to be influenced by someone's unique features. A common makeup artist reaction is to try to create makeup technique as it applies only to this person's face.

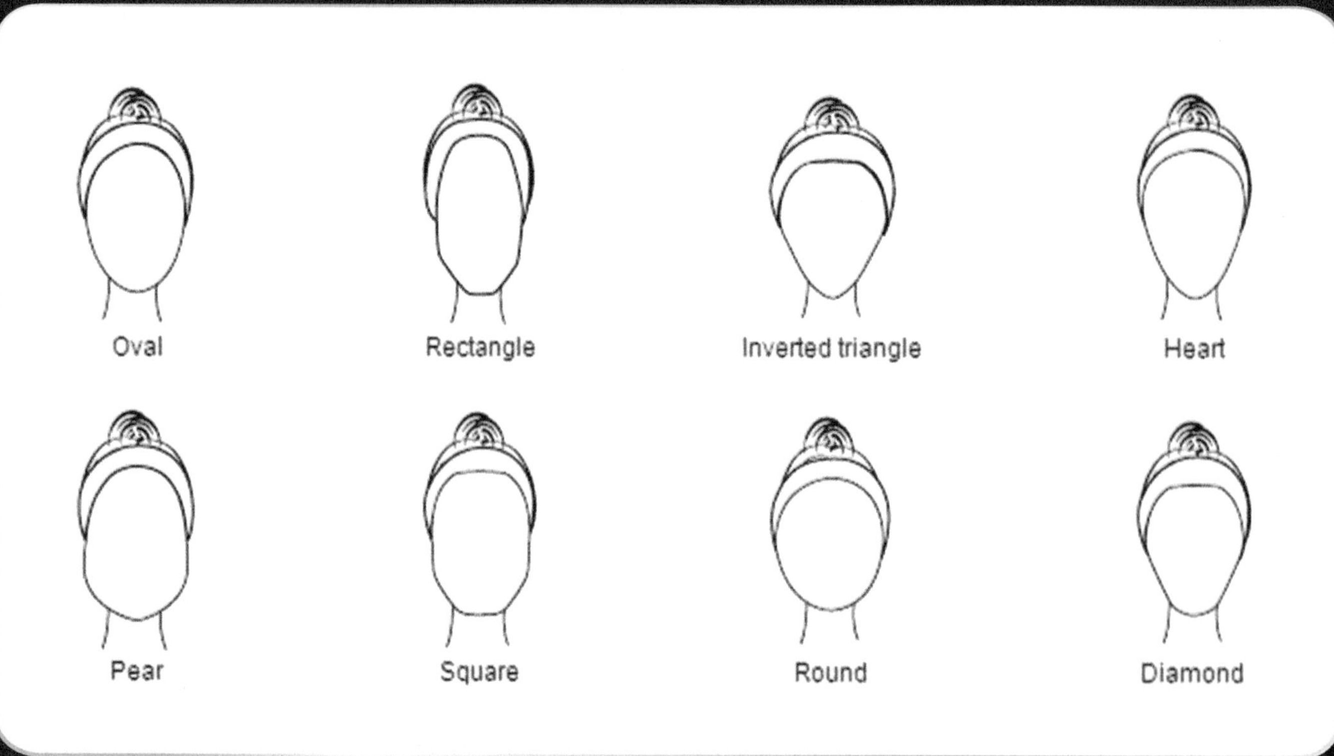

This is especially reinforced when having hair styled by an aesthetically sensitive hairdresser. They will, quite deeply, take into consideration a style that best complements a client's face shape and features.

Knowing this, aesthetically aware individuals want to know from a professional perspective their face shape and how to best complement it with makeup.

There are many individual makeup artistry techniques dedicated to all the intricacies of different face shapes. They are all valid and learned over time.

The theory for makeup enclosed here focuses on a universal method of makeup application. It highlights the essential shape of Every Face. This shape is the Heart of the Face. This method will quickly and effectively bring every face shape into beautiful proportion.

Face with a Heart

For the purposes of this manual, a standardized face chart will be used to illustrate all of the theories and techniques.

Please know that all of these theories and techniques apply to all the face shapes (and more) illustrated in the previous chapter.

Regardless of any face shape, illuminating the heart of the face always produces the most aesthetically pleasing/beautiful and symmetrically balanced results.

It is literally that center of the face, when isolated, is the shape of a heart.

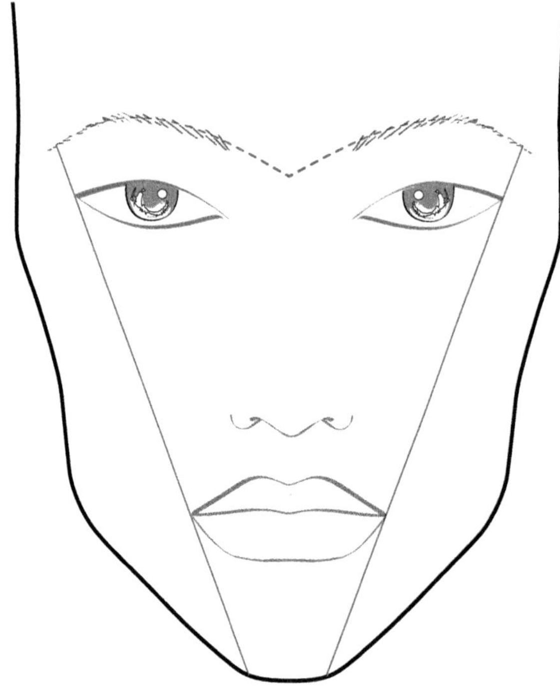

The heart of the face starts with the eyebrows being the top of the heart.

As they arch around the outer corner of the eyes, the line continues in a straight line down past the outer corners of the lips.

The line then continues to merge into a "V" at the base of the chin.

This is the literal, objective heart of the face.

This shape reinforces the theoretical concept that beauty is symmetry. It is calming when features are in balance and generally psychologically pleasing.

Within and outside of this literal heart of the face are smaller geometrical shapes that continue to create symmetry within symmetry.

These geometrical shapes are what the makeup artist uses as the guide to create a beautiful makeup.

Face Shape Translator

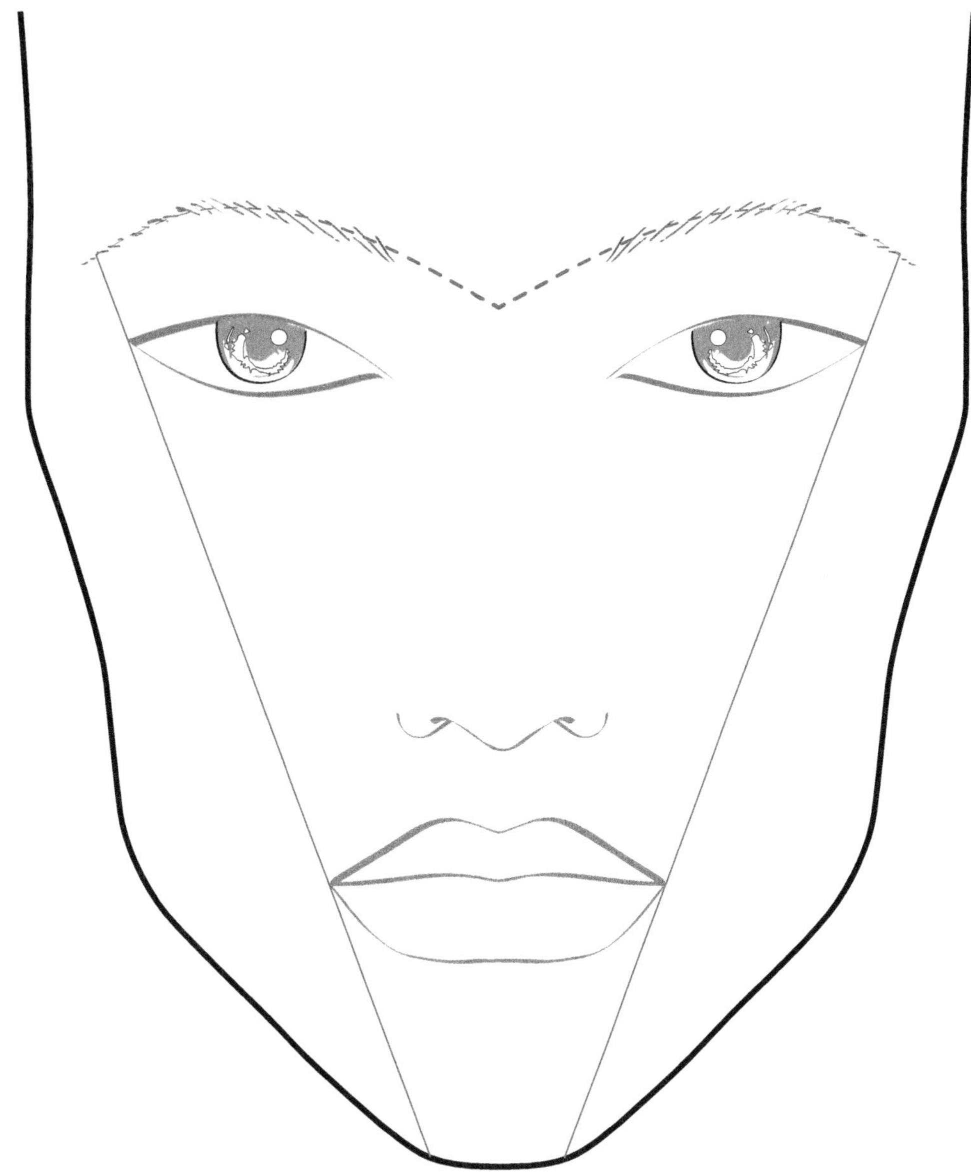

Here are all the before mentioned face shapes and how the Face with a Heart grid translates to each face shape. The beauty of this heart grid is that it automatically provides precise placement for the makeup application to the anatomy of any face shape.

Diamond face shape

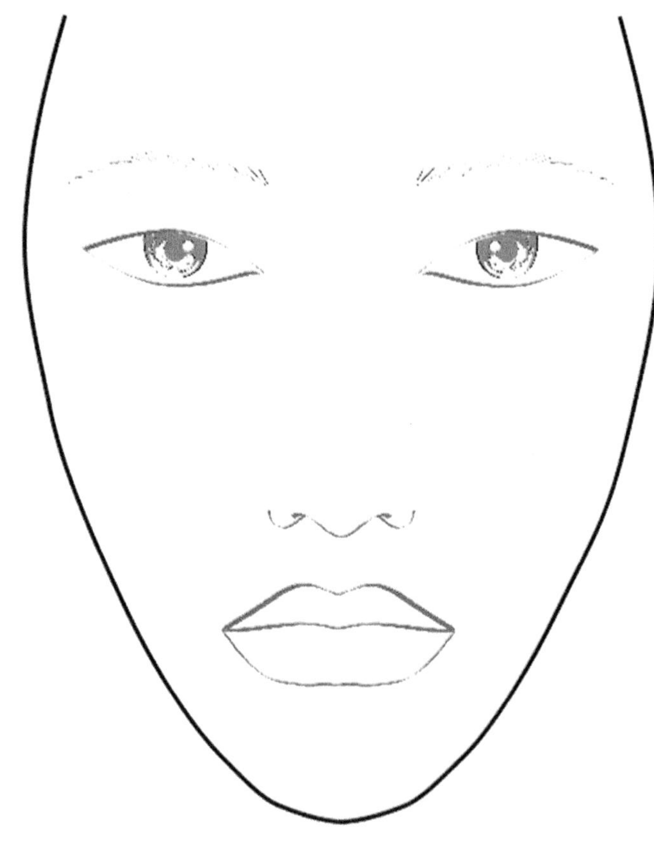

Diamond face shape with Heart Grid

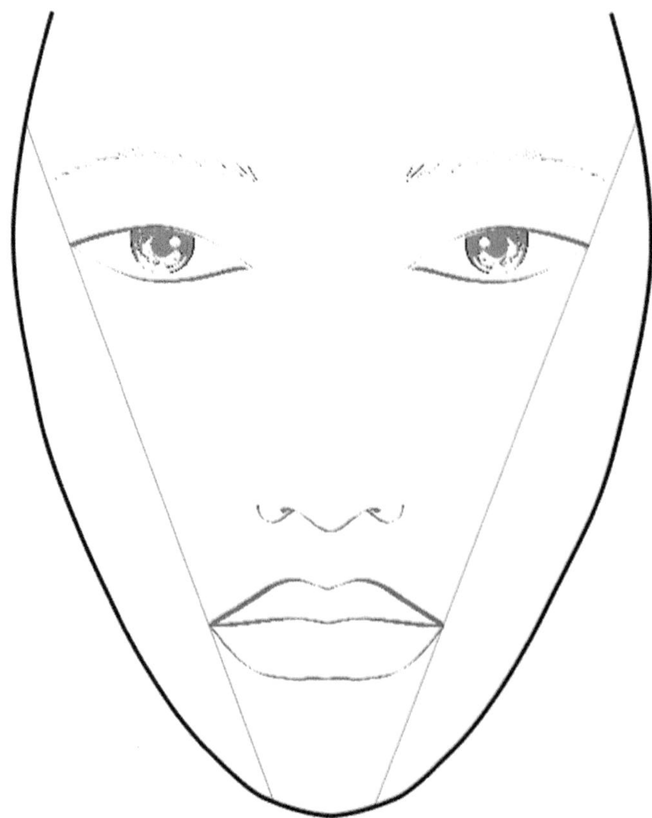

Heart face shape

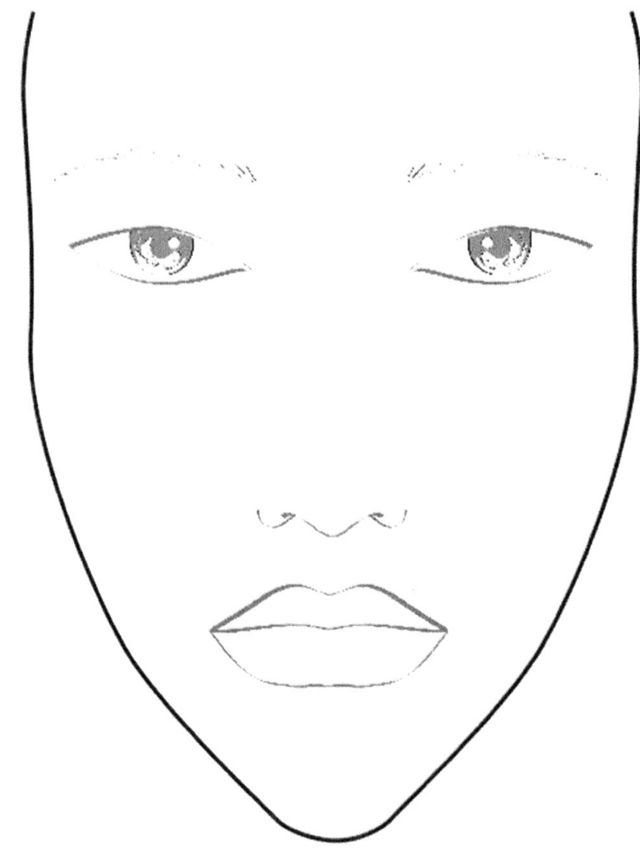

Heart face shape with Heart Grid

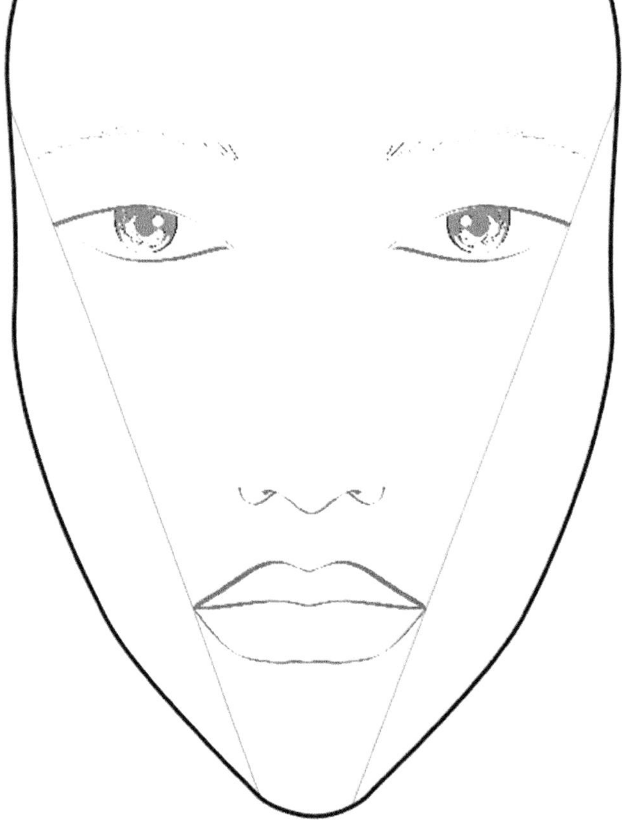

Inverted triangle face shape

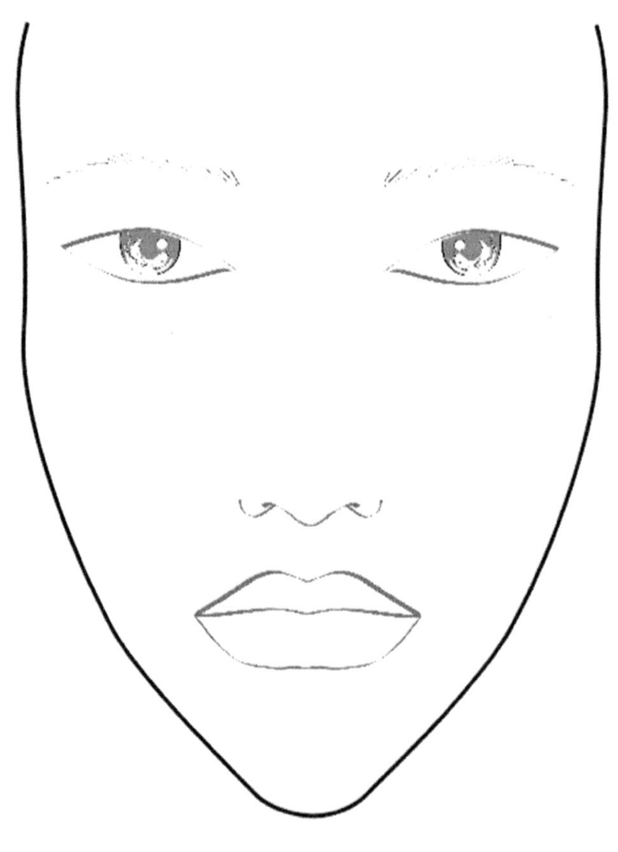

Inverted triangle face shape with Heart Grid

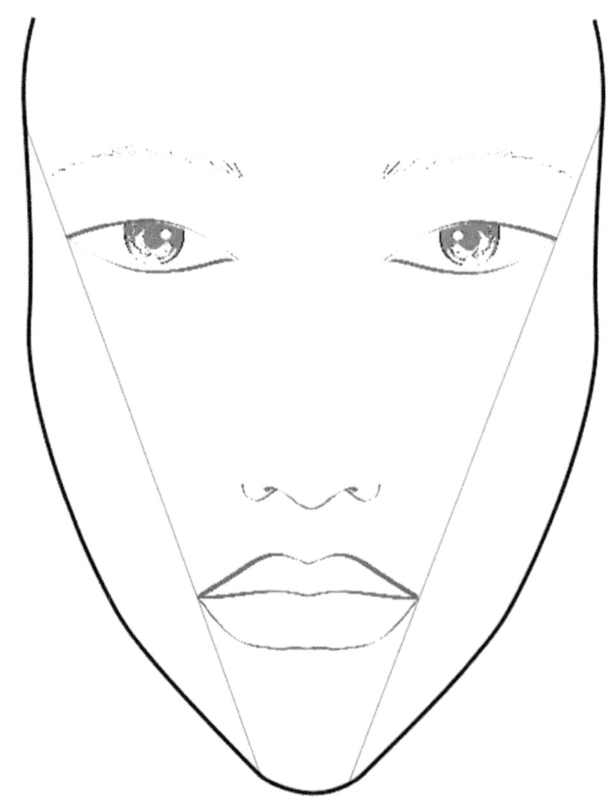

Oblong face shape

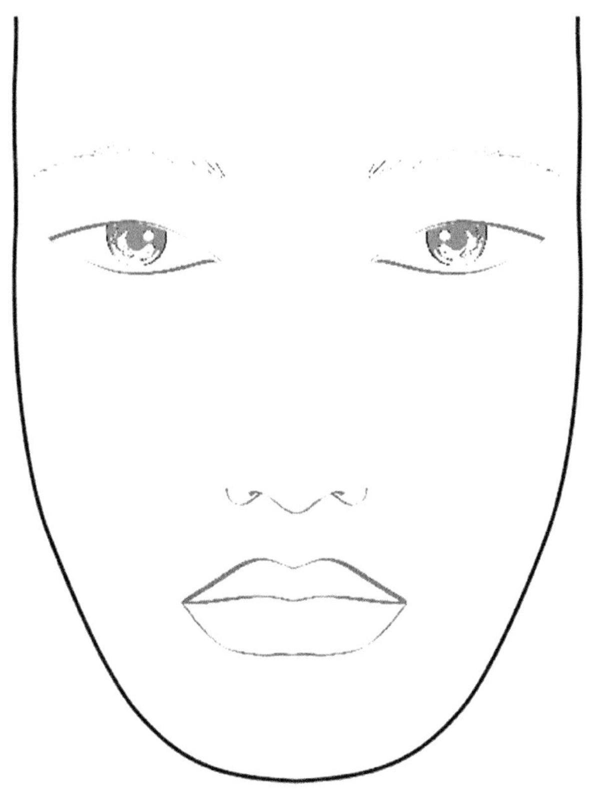

Oblong face shape with Heart Grid

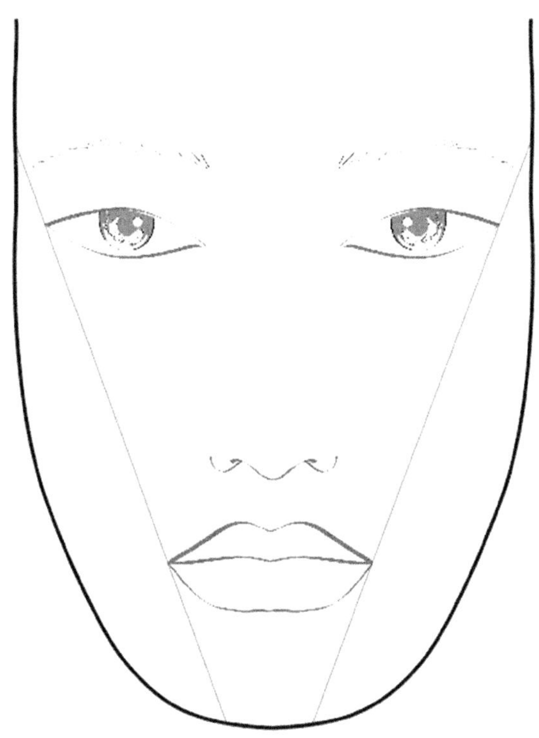

Oval face shape

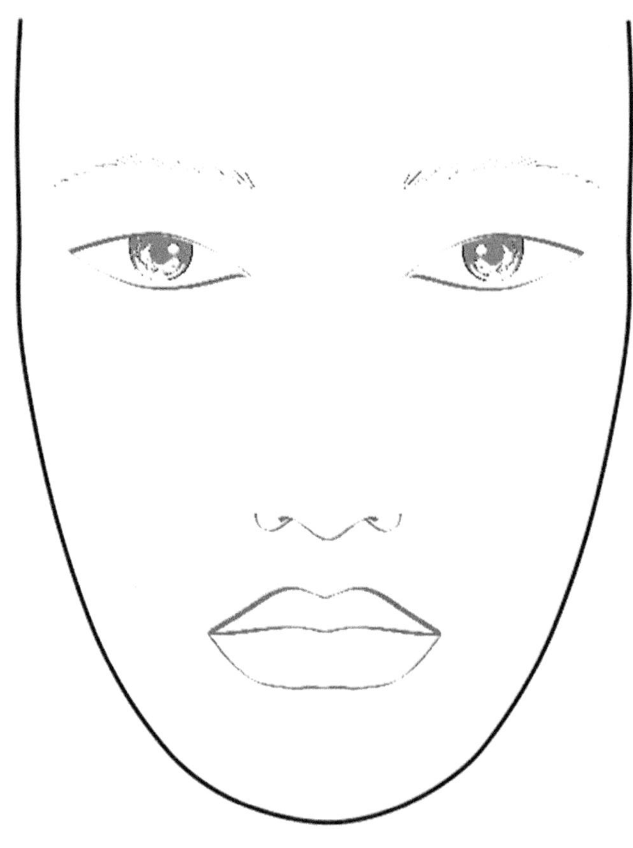

Oval face shape with Heart Grid

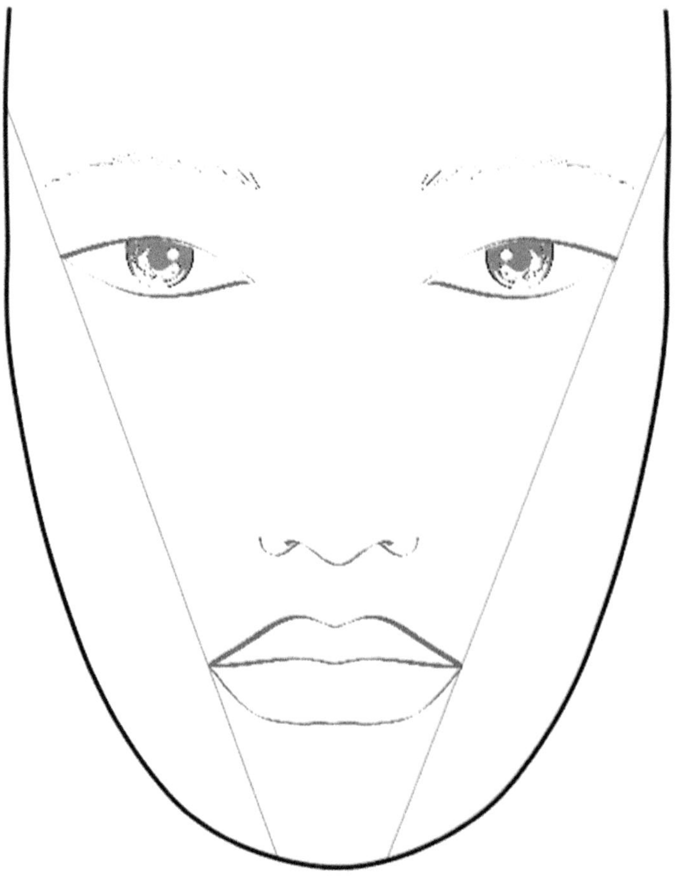

Rectangular face shape

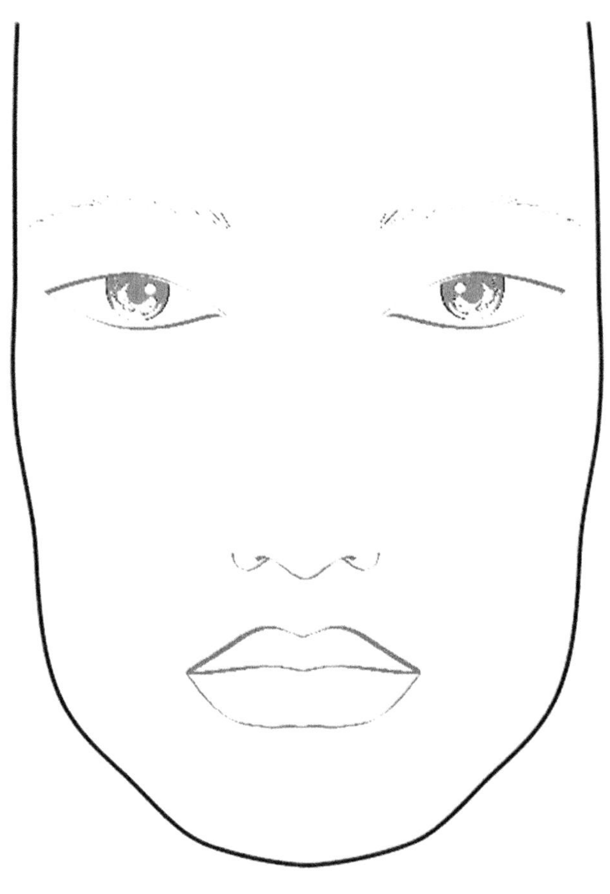

Rectangular face shape with Heart Grid

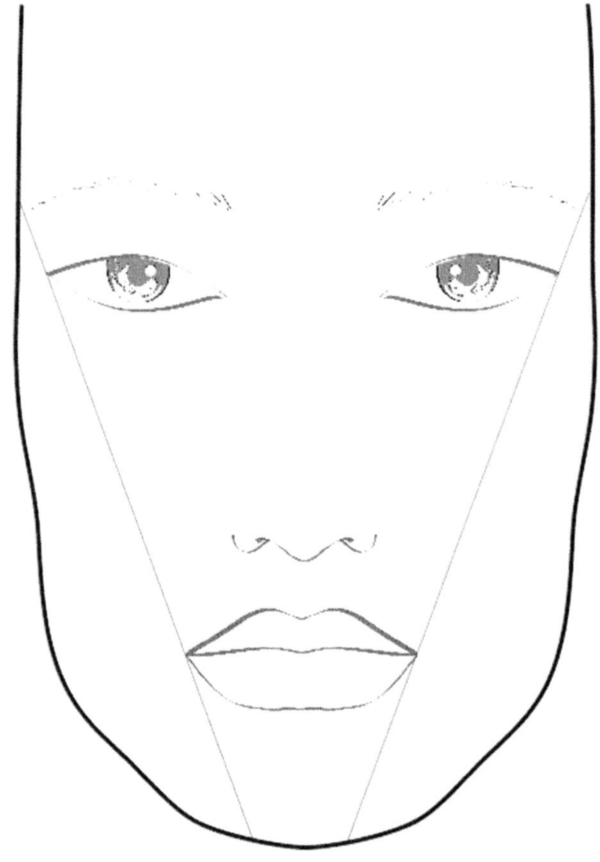

Round face shape

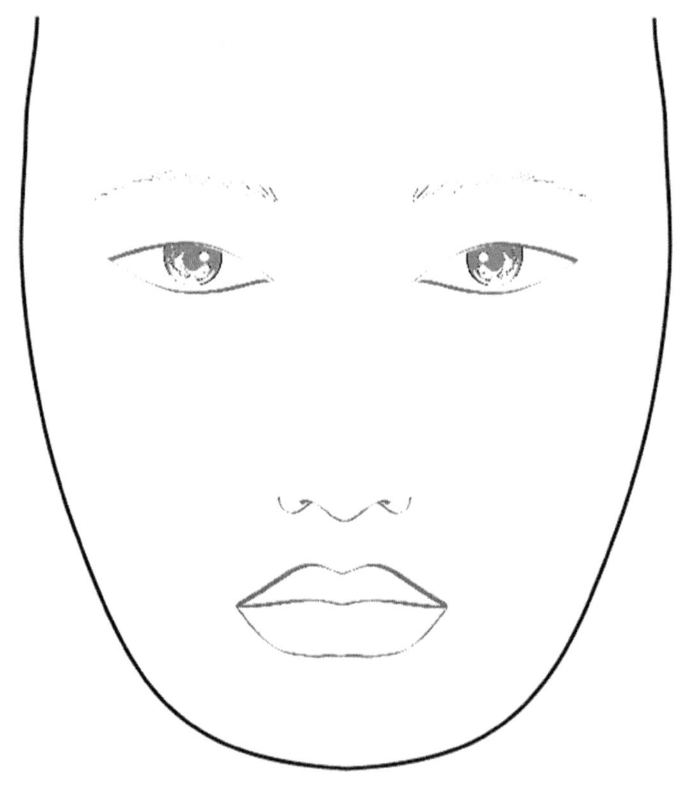

Round face shape with Heart Grid

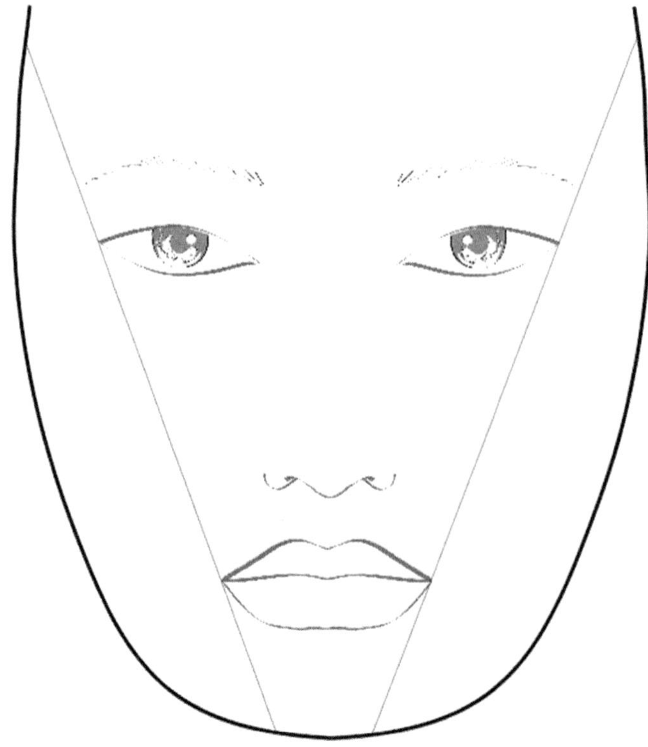

Square face shape

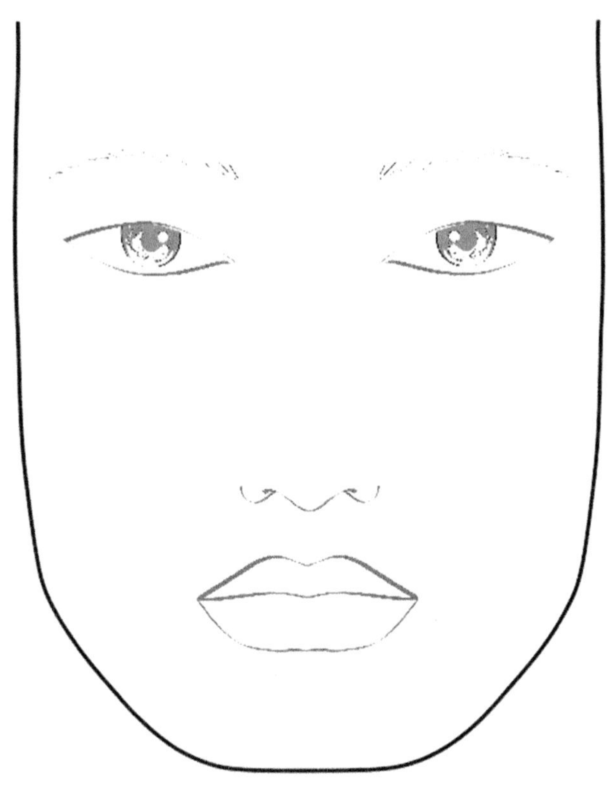

Square face shape with Heart Grid

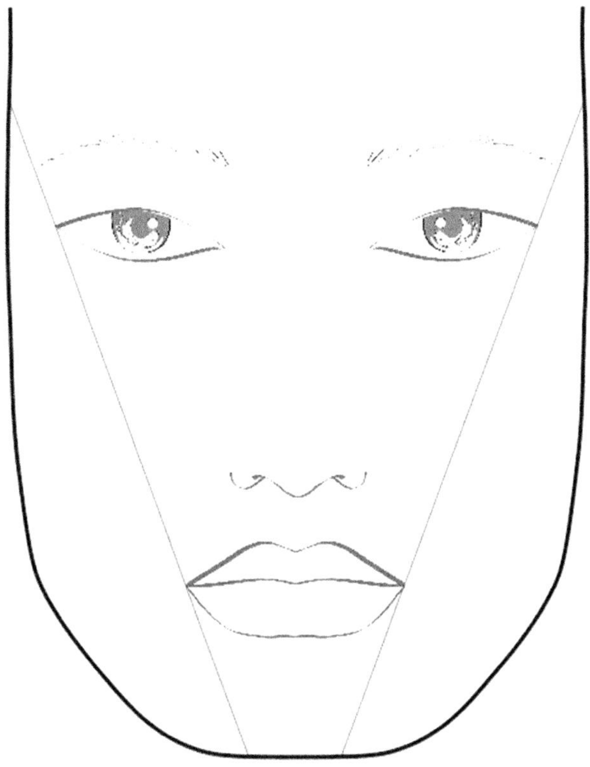

Triangular (Pear) face shape

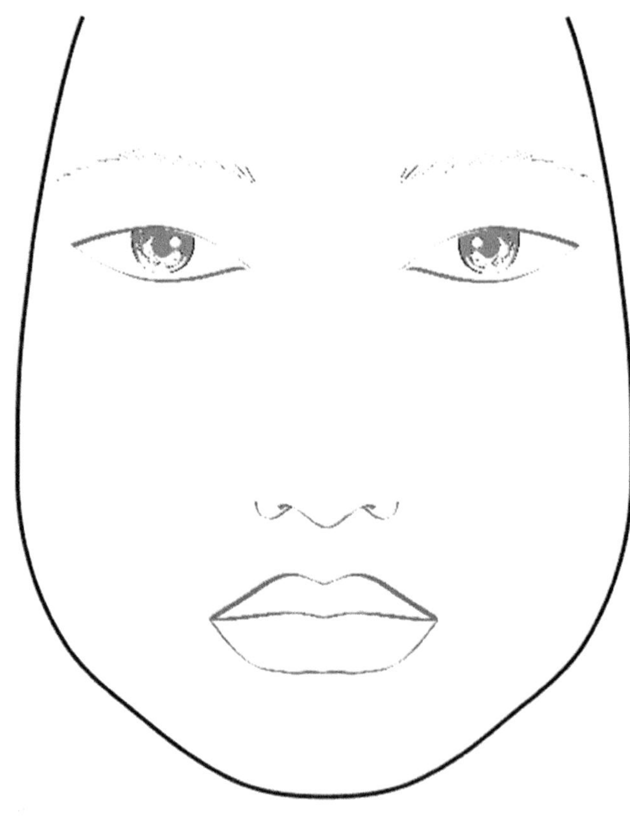

Triangular (Pear) face shape with Heart Grid

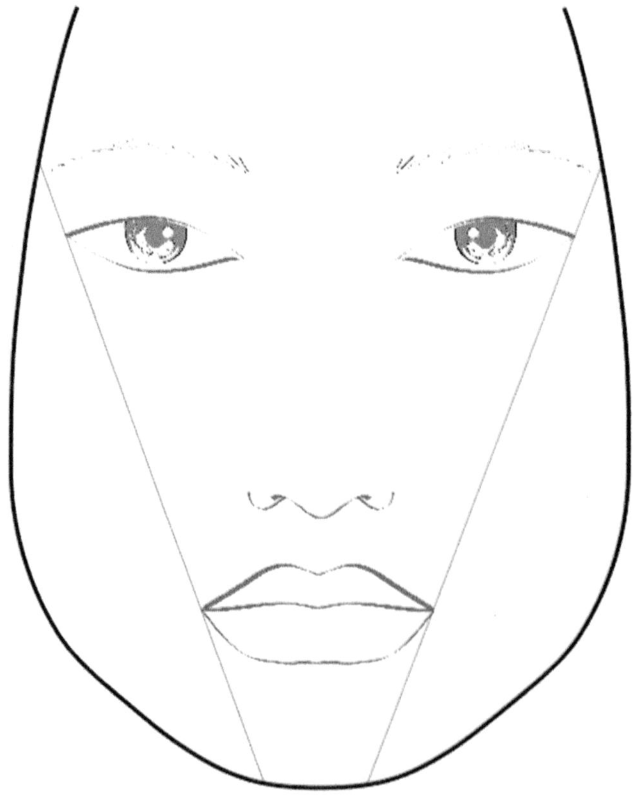

The reason so many face shapes are shown is to help a makeup artist or a makeup enthusiast see the universality of the Face with a Heart. Too often with makeup, people focus on the aspects of their features they like least. Finding a way to focus on what really matters by using this 'V' like grid, will allow others to focus on the part of you that matters most.

Reduce the Distractions/ Enhance the Attractions

Makeup and makeup artistry is a constant series of observations and decisions. It is important that with every face the makeup artist freshly revisit these observations and make decisions based on the face he or she is currently working on.

One of the best skills a makeup artist can develop is identifying both the positive (attractions) and negative (distractions) aspects of a models face as it pertains to the look of the makeup.

As a rule, on every face, distractions need to be neutralized before adding any makeup to enhance the attractions. If the artist doesn't do this, then they over compensate with makeup to make the attractions pop by trying to pull focus from distractions on the face.

What are attractions?

- Eyes
- Lips
- Heart of the face
- Cheekbones

In all beauty makeup, it is the goal of the makeup to deftly isolate the eyes and lips so that they are the features that are noticed first and remembered last.

What are distractions?

- Darkness under the eye
- Redness
- Shadows created by folds in the skin
- Blemishes
- Patchy hyper pigmentation

These are the most obvious culprits in the distraction game.

The makeup artist will find that when he or she takes a moment to identify the distractions noticed before the eyes and lips, and then neutralize these distractions, it is then easier to make the attractions pop.

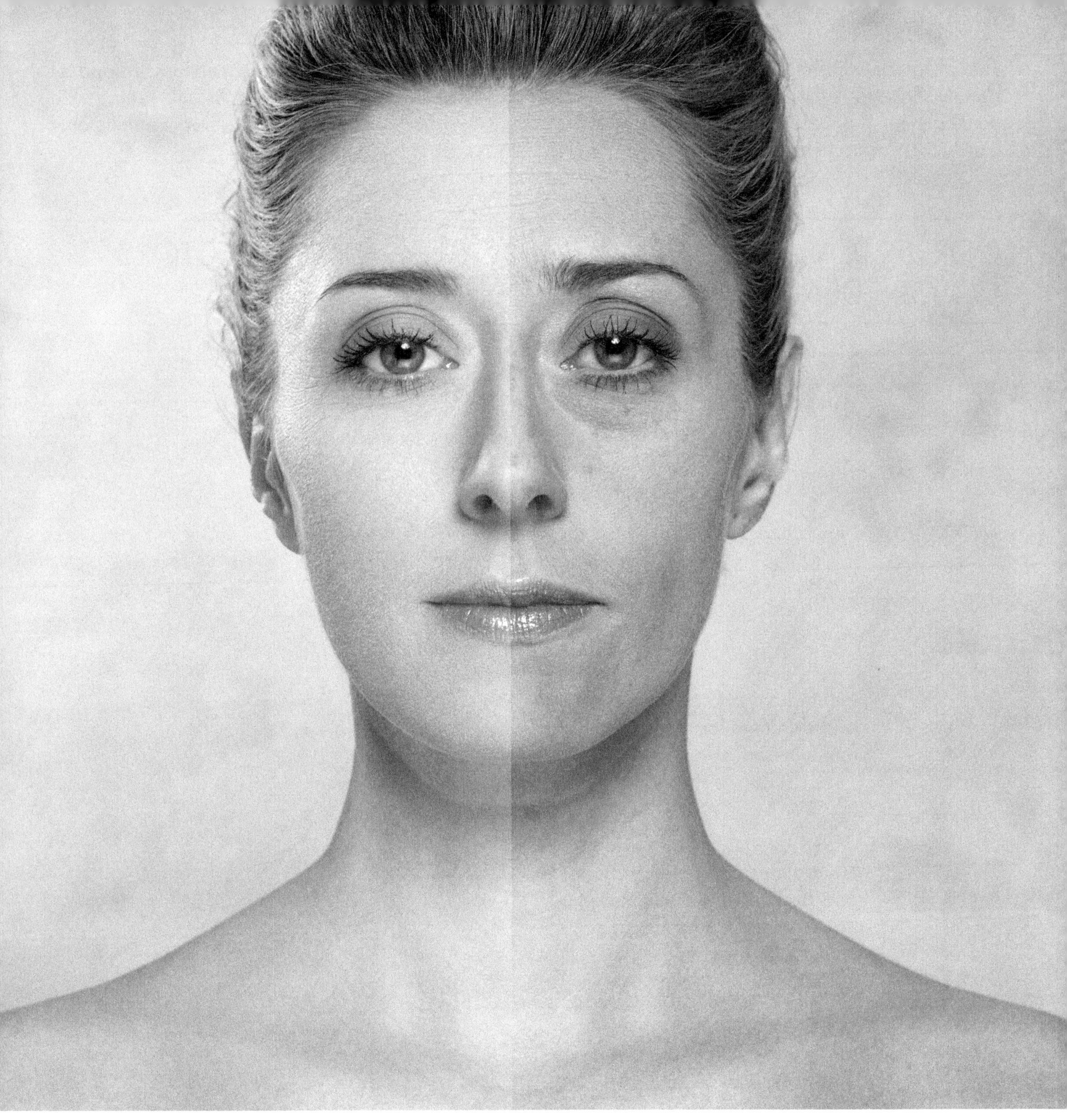

Great makeup is a perfect balance between what we want to see and what we don't want to see. Overcompensation in any one direction makes for an imbalanced makeup that draws attention to the makeup and not the person wearing it.

One of the biggest offenders of overcompensation is under eye concealer. The makeup artist works so hard to cover up any sign of darkness that they leave behind a thick half-moon shape under the eye that, in its own way, acts as a distraction. First the product is applied so heavily that it pulls focus from the eye. Secondly, by not utilizing the grid concept of the face, the circles under the eye are reinforced rather than redirecting the under eye shape outwards and upwards so it lifts and expands the eye rather than diminish and distract from it.

The greatest adjustment in achieving authentic beauty makeup is the art of correction instead of concealment.

Correctors are unexpected shades of makeup that neutralize darkness and redness instead of covering it up. The win here is still seeing skin when it is corrected; when it is concealed, only the makeup is seen.

CORRECTOR COLORS DEFINED		SKIN TONE	CORRECTORS
Pink	Neutralizes and corrects darkness and brightens for light to medium skin tones	Light	
Green	Neutralizes and corrects redness for light to medium skin tones	Medium Light	
Light Yellow	Neutralizes and corrects redness and darkness for medium to medium-dark skin tones.	Medium	
Dark Yellow	Neutralizes and corrects redness and darkness for medium-dark to dark skin tones.(interchangeable with orange, depending on skin's undertone)	Medium Dark	
Orange	Neutralizes and corrects redness and darkness for medium-dark to dark skin tones. (interchangeable with deep yellow, depending on skin's undertone)	Dark	

World of the Eye

After the Heart of the Face grid, the second most important grid is the World of the Eye grid. The eyes are the most expressive part of the face and where the most attention is paid with makeup. By following these guidelines you will always maximize a client's eyes – never diminish or exaggerate them.

Most eyes, regardless of their overall shape, have basic similar characteristics;
the eyebrow at the top of the eye and a lash line under the eye. This creates the top and bottom border to your eye makeup.

The side borders of the eye are dictated by another grid which originates at the nose flare and extends in two upwards and outward directions.
One line goes from the nose flare up past the inner corner of the eye

The other line goes from the nose flare past the outer corner of the eye.

This creates an angled 'V' shape from the nose flare past the inner and outer corner of the eye. The area between the two lines of the 'V' and the eyebrow and bottom lash line is the World of the Eye. It is within this world we can breakdown the dynamic of the eye even further.

The First shape to note is the eyebrow. The eyebrow touches both ends of the 'V'.

It does not extend past nor stop within the 'V'; it extends completely from one side to the other. Matching this shape on both sides sets up the most critical element of symmetry: balanced eyebrows.

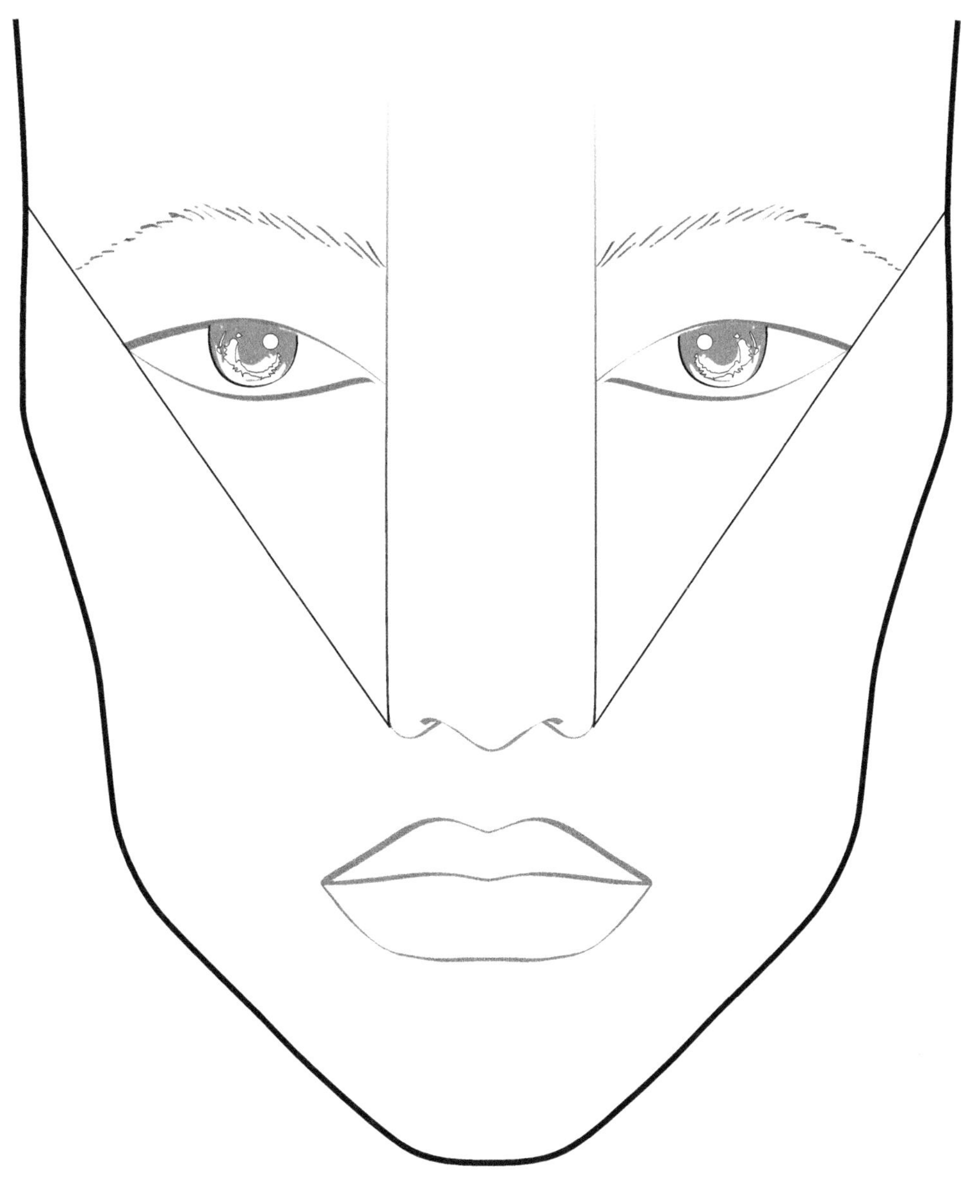

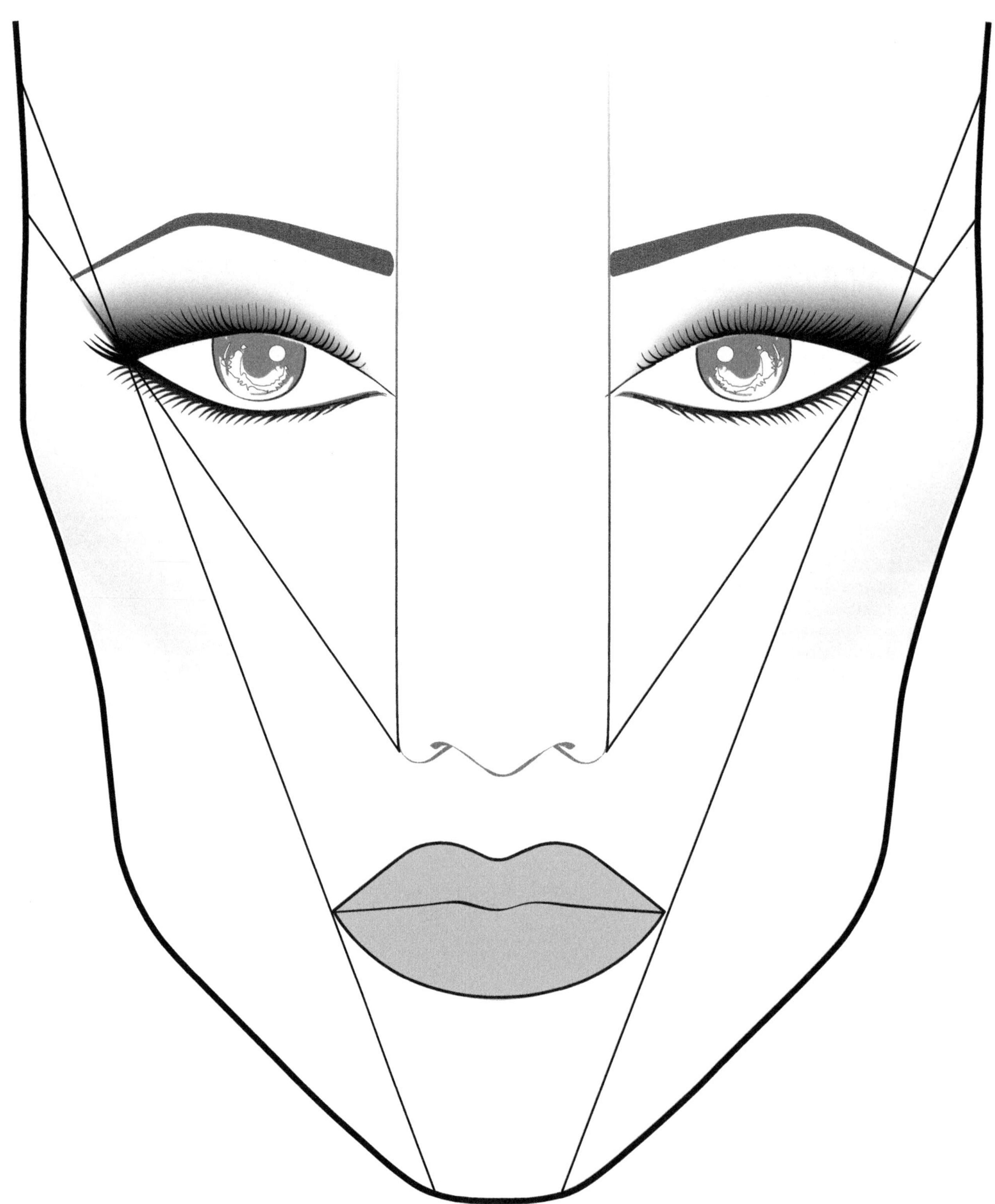

In order to maximize the eye, the borders of the World of the Eye grid must be respected. To work beyond the eyebrows will exaggerate the eye. To work inside them will diminish the eye. To work up to the borders of the grids will maximize the organic and authentic shape of the eye.

Sweet Spot of the Eye

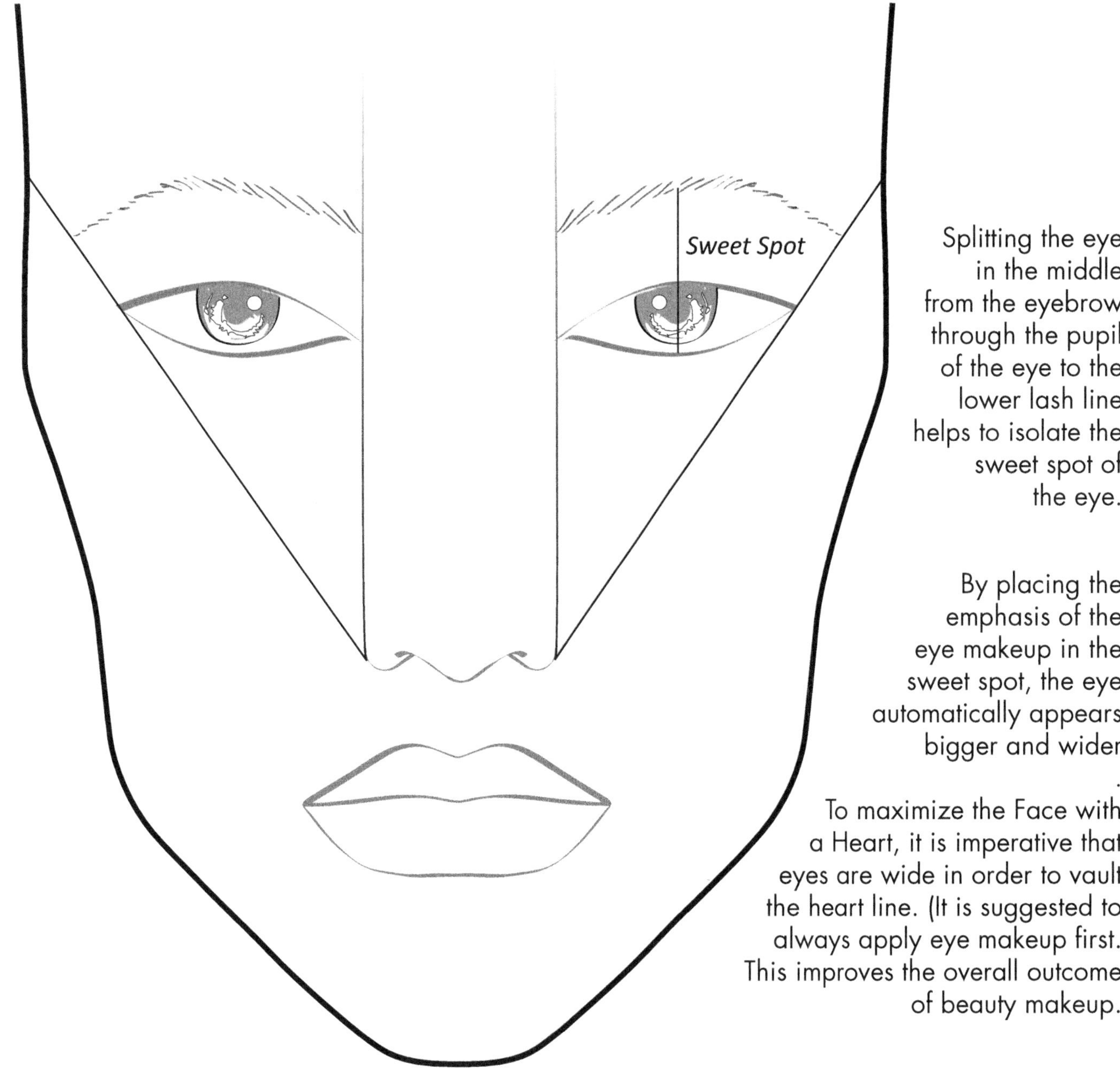

Splitting the eye in the middle from the eyebrow through the pupil of the eye to the lower lash line helps to isolate the sweet spot of the eye.

By placing the emphasis of the eye makeup in the sweet spot, the eye automatically appears bigger and wider

.

To maximize the Face with a Heart, it is imperative that eyes are wide in order to vault the heart line. (It is suggested to always apply eye makeup first. This improves the overall outcome of beauty makeup.

The Vault of the Face

Vault means the energy lift created by the upward and outward lines of the 'heart of the face' and 'world of the eye' grids.

There is a desire to create a generally lifted look to the features of the face.
Most people want:

- Their eyes to lift /rise up and outwards
- The corners of their mouth to lift upwards
- They want their cheek bones high and apparent
- They want their jawline straight and tapering in towards the chin

Most people do not want:

- Their eyes to droop and appear tired
- Their mouth to appear as a frown when they are relaxed
- Their cheekbones non-existent
- Their jawline to droop and reflect an appearance of aging

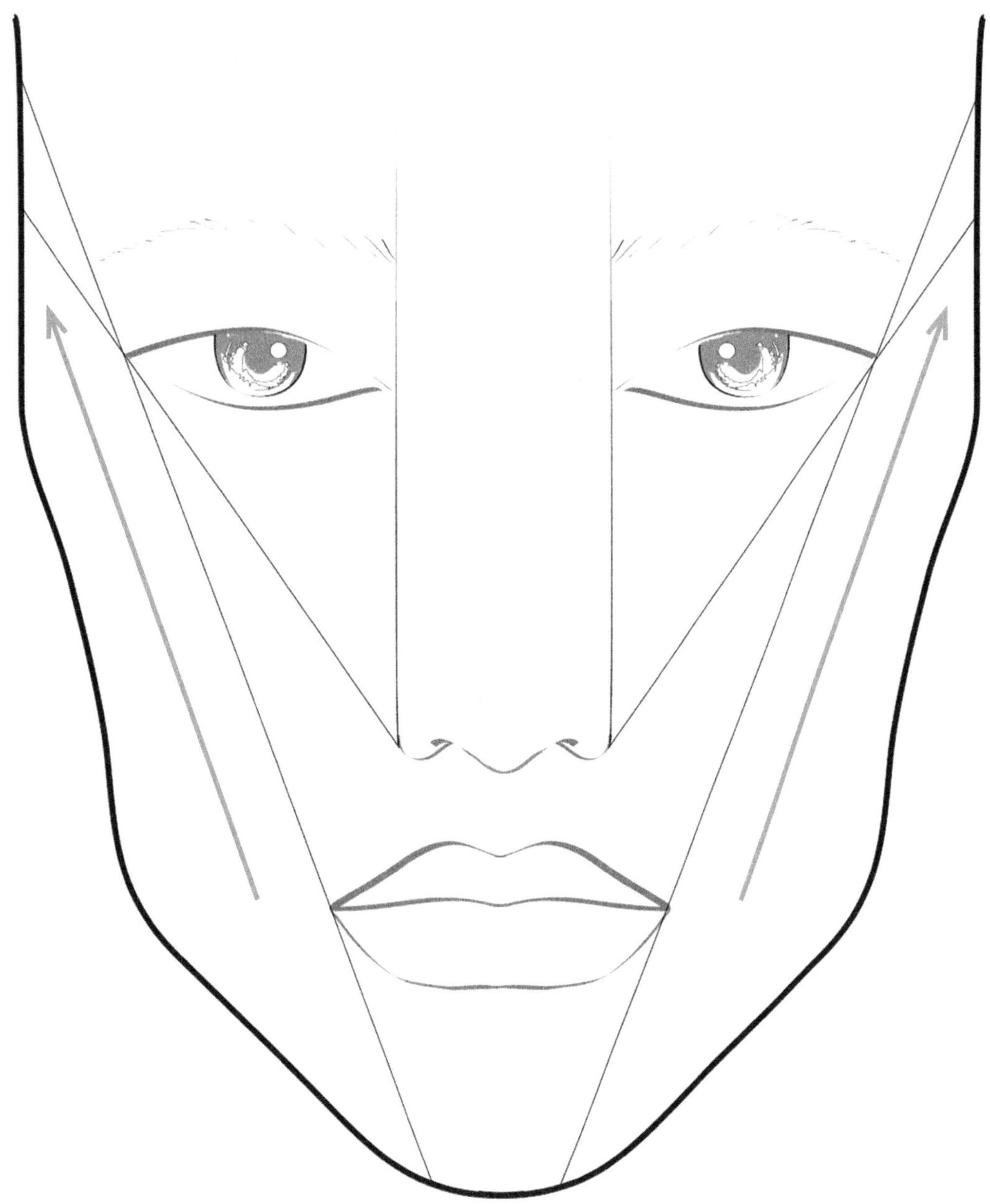

This is why using the Face with a Heart approach to makeup is so effective for every face. The powerful upward and outward lines used to direct the flow of makeup all work in conjunction to create the best overall lifted look.

Although the invisible heart grid lines we use to direct our makeup are straight, the visual effect is an opening 'V' shape that starts at the chin and appears to curve slightly outward as it makes its way up the face. This gentle progression of vaulting energy/light is what creates and maintains the upward structure to all of the facial features.

As the heart line reaches up from the outer corner of the lips to the outer corner of the eyes, the face vaults upward and outward as it connects to the World of the Eye grid.

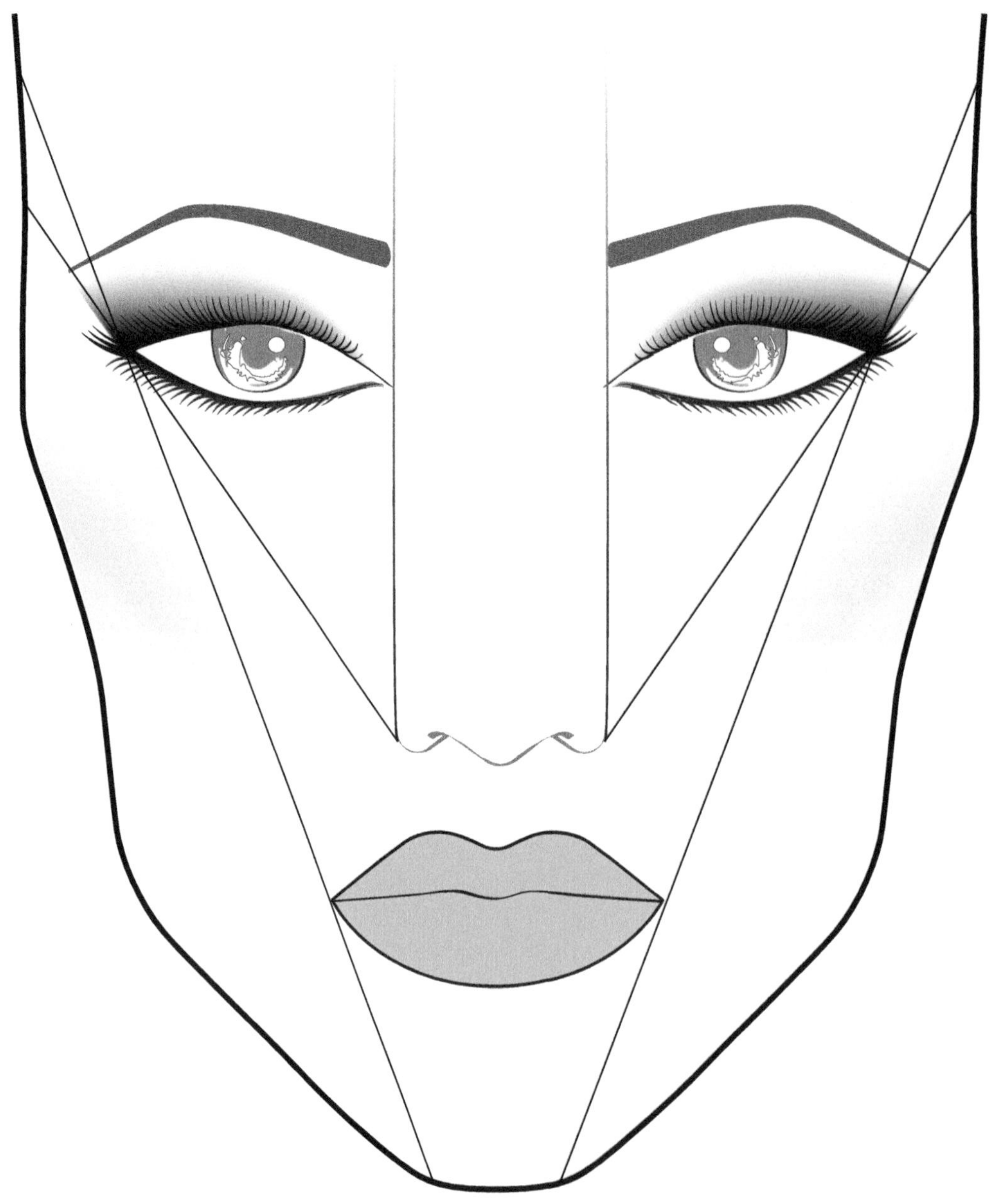

As an artist, it is imperative to create this beautiful, lifting, vaulting energy/light on every face to maximize the desired 'wants' that most people strive for on their face.

A makeup artist can apply many smaller techniques to the eyes, lips, cheeks, including facial contouring to support and enhance this vaulting energy. These smaller techniques will only add to the overall effect of the Face with a Heart technique of makeup application.

Visualizing the concept of lifting, vaulting energy/light, and then employing this concept on every makeup will enhance the makeup applied. As an artist, it is vital to distinguish yourself by possessing unique skills that make your work stand alone, apart, and above the rest, making yourself truly vital and one-of-a-kind.

Eyes Wide/ Lips Tall

Lips Tall

Lips are at the narrow end of the 'V' on the face that encompasses the heart. To maximize the effect of the heart shape, focus on the fullness and roundness at the center of the lips and avoid over extending the outer corners of the lips. By doing so, the lips will achieve a vital fullness in the center where it counts, and the heart line drawing up from the sides of the lips towards the outer corner of the eyes will not be too wide at the base of the chin.

There are many finishes that can be achieved with the lips including;

- Stain
- Creamy
- Matte
- Glossy
- Satin
- Neutral

Regardless of the finish for the lip, maximizing the height of the lips rather than the width will contribute to a heightened sense of 'vault' and 'heart' to the face, and will achieve maximum beauty makeup success.

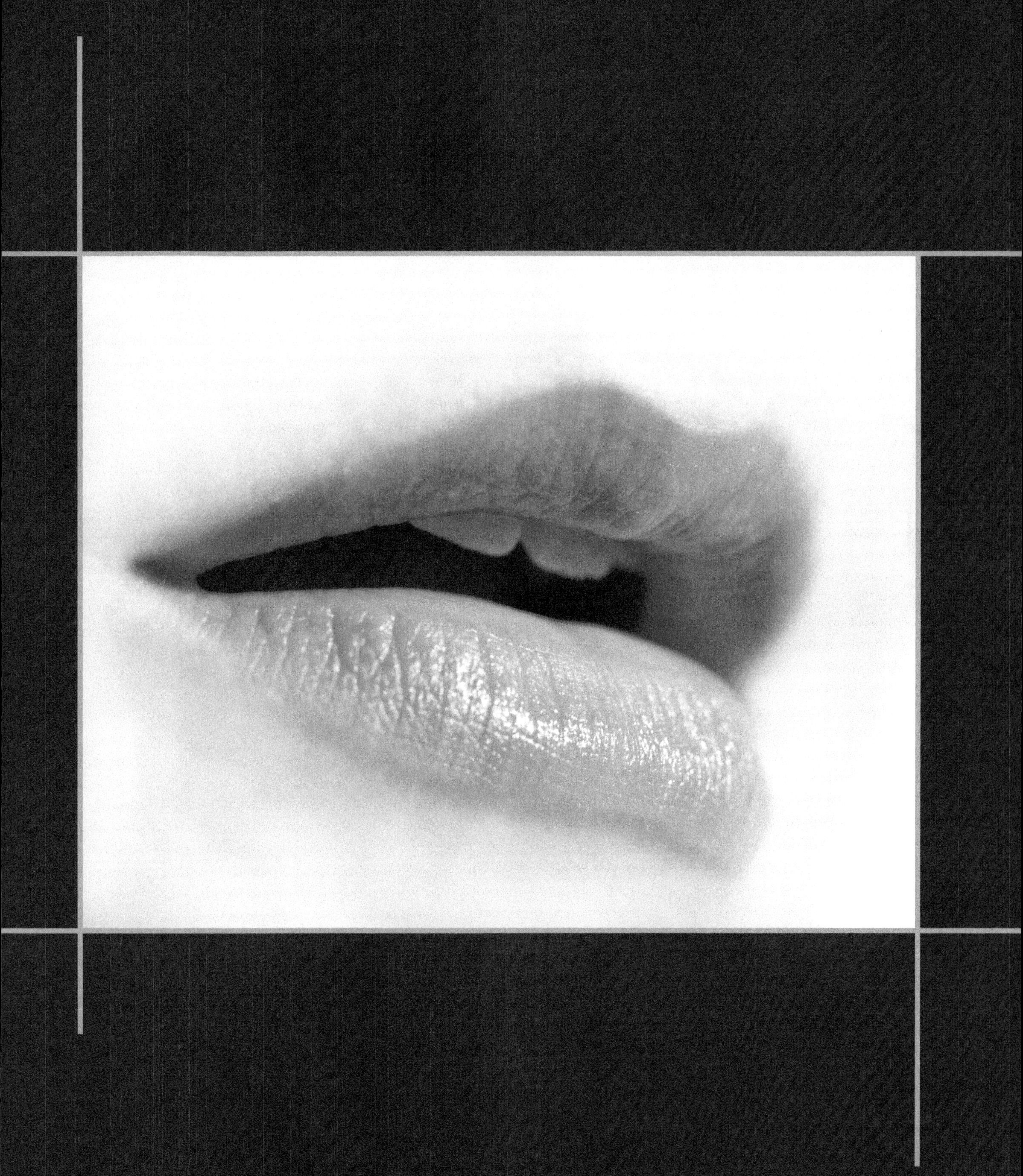

Cheeks Frame the Heart

In order to maximize the other features of the face and the makeup techniques being employed with this training manual, cheeks ALWAYS come after eyes, foundation, and lips have been applied. There is no other way to know how to balance your cheek makeup to the main attractions – eyes and lips – until after the eyes and lips have been applied and skin has been neutralized.

With beauty makeup, applying blush, contour, bronzing powder or highlights must always support the main attractions. The cheeks must always enhance the main attractions and direct the attention more to the eyes and lips rather than away.

All of the approaches to shaping and brightening the exterior of the heart are valid. The individual look must dictate which techniques are appropriate for each look.

Lash Last

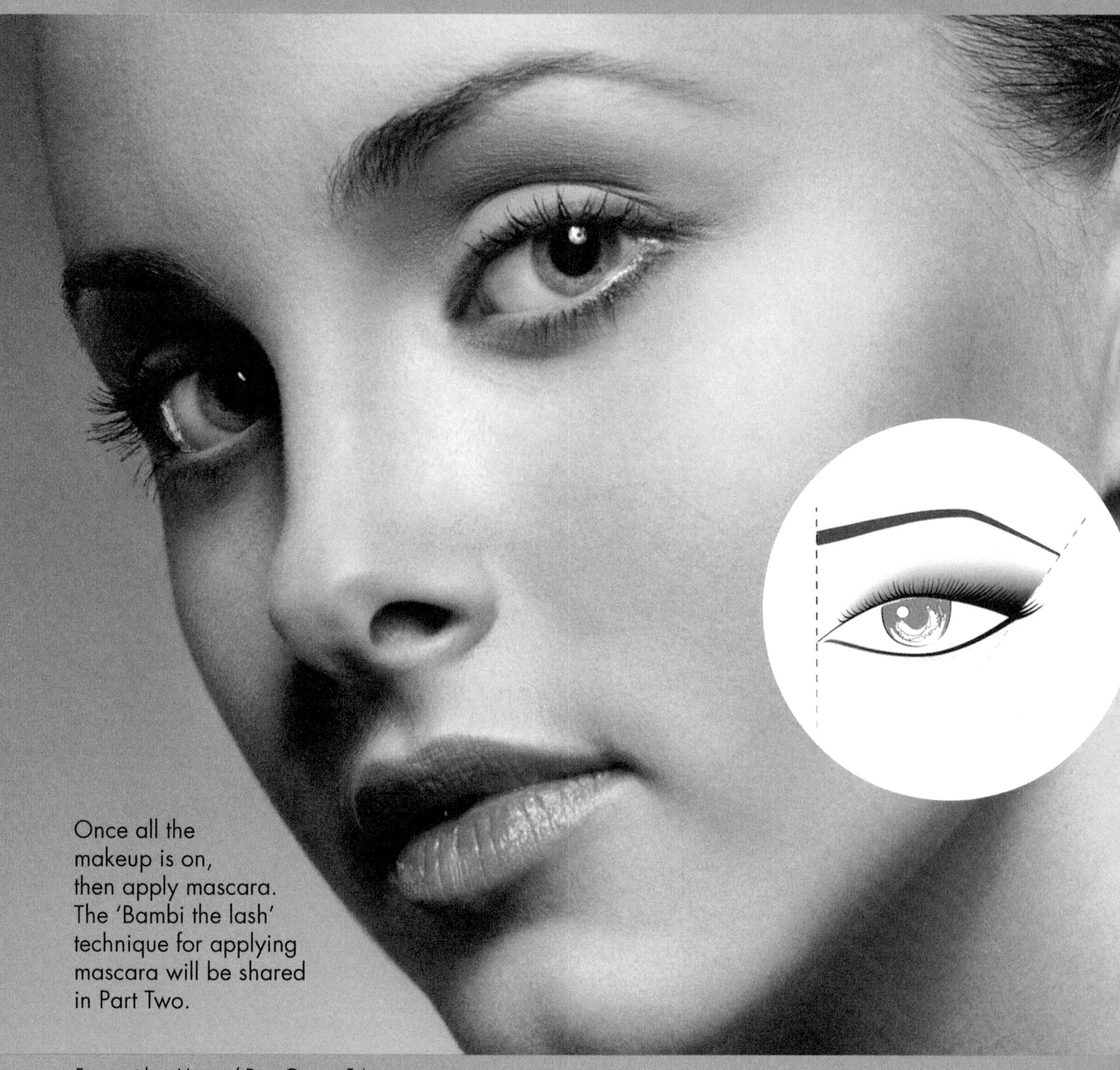

Once all the makeup is on, then apply mascara. The 'Bambi the lash' technique for applying mascara will be shared in Part Two.

The Whole is Greater than the Sum of its Parts

Aristotle said, *"The whole is greater than the sum of its parts,"* and this definitely applies to makeup. After completing the makeup application, step back to see all of these little techniques which by themselves may not seem significant, work in concert on the face as a whole. The end result ends up looking better than all the little parts used to put the look together.

Looking real close at a beautiful painting creates the same phenomenon. At a certain point the picture disappears and only the technique the artist used to create the effect can be seen. Then backing away allows the detail of the technique to disappear and the beautiful painting re-emerges.

This is exactly what happens every time a makeup artist applies makeup. The artist must be close to apply the makeup and see the details of the technique, and then the artist steps away to see the effect of the technique and take in the look as a whole.

During the course of a makeup application, remember to step away from the model (or the mirror in the case of self-application) periodically throughout the application to maintain perspective and symmetry with the affect the detailed technique is creating as a whole.

In Part Two, every technique will be broken down to achieve a Face with a Heart and Authentic Beauty Makeup will be mastered.

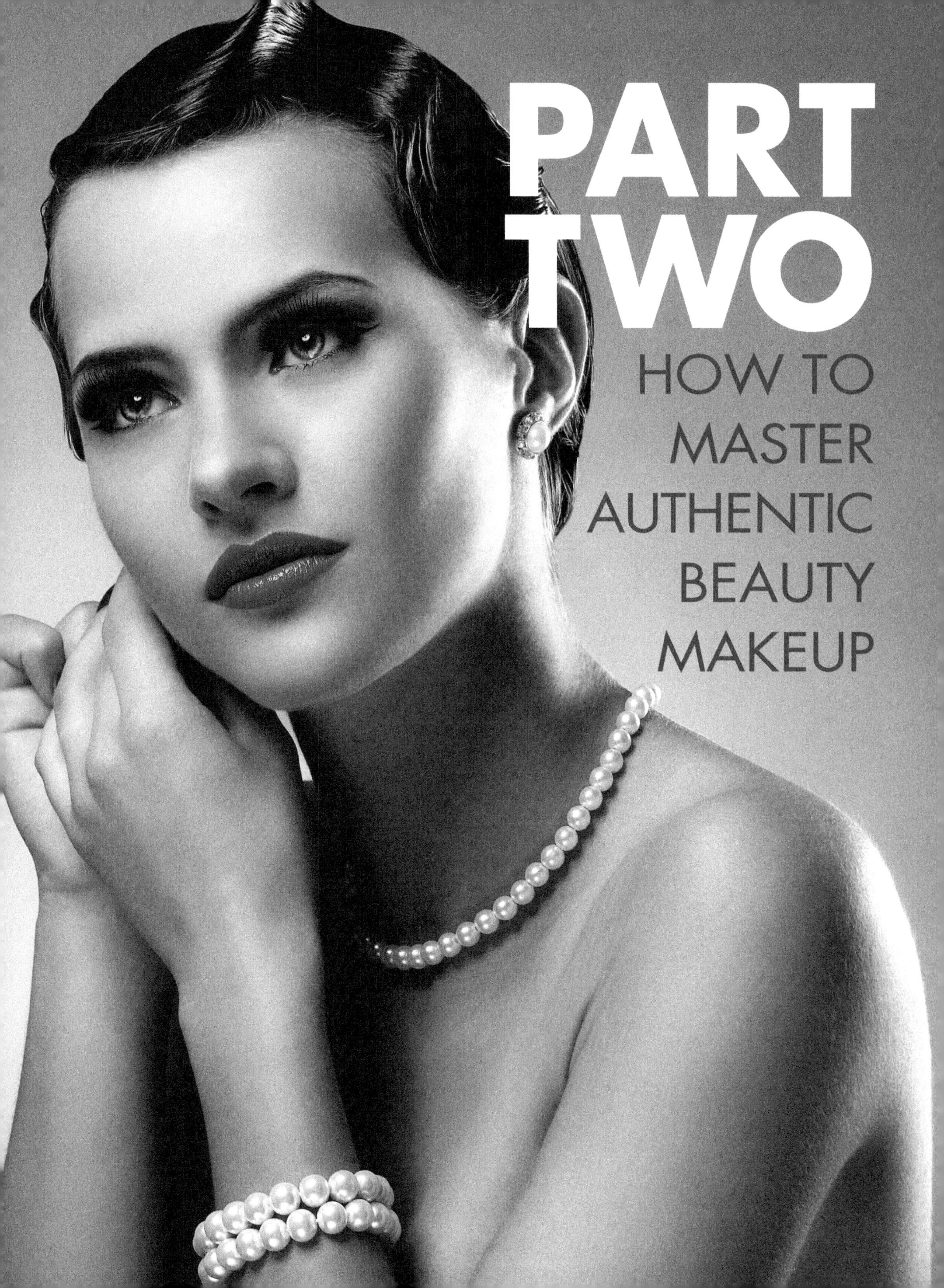

PART TWO

HOW TO MASTER AUTHENTIC BEAUTY MAKEUP

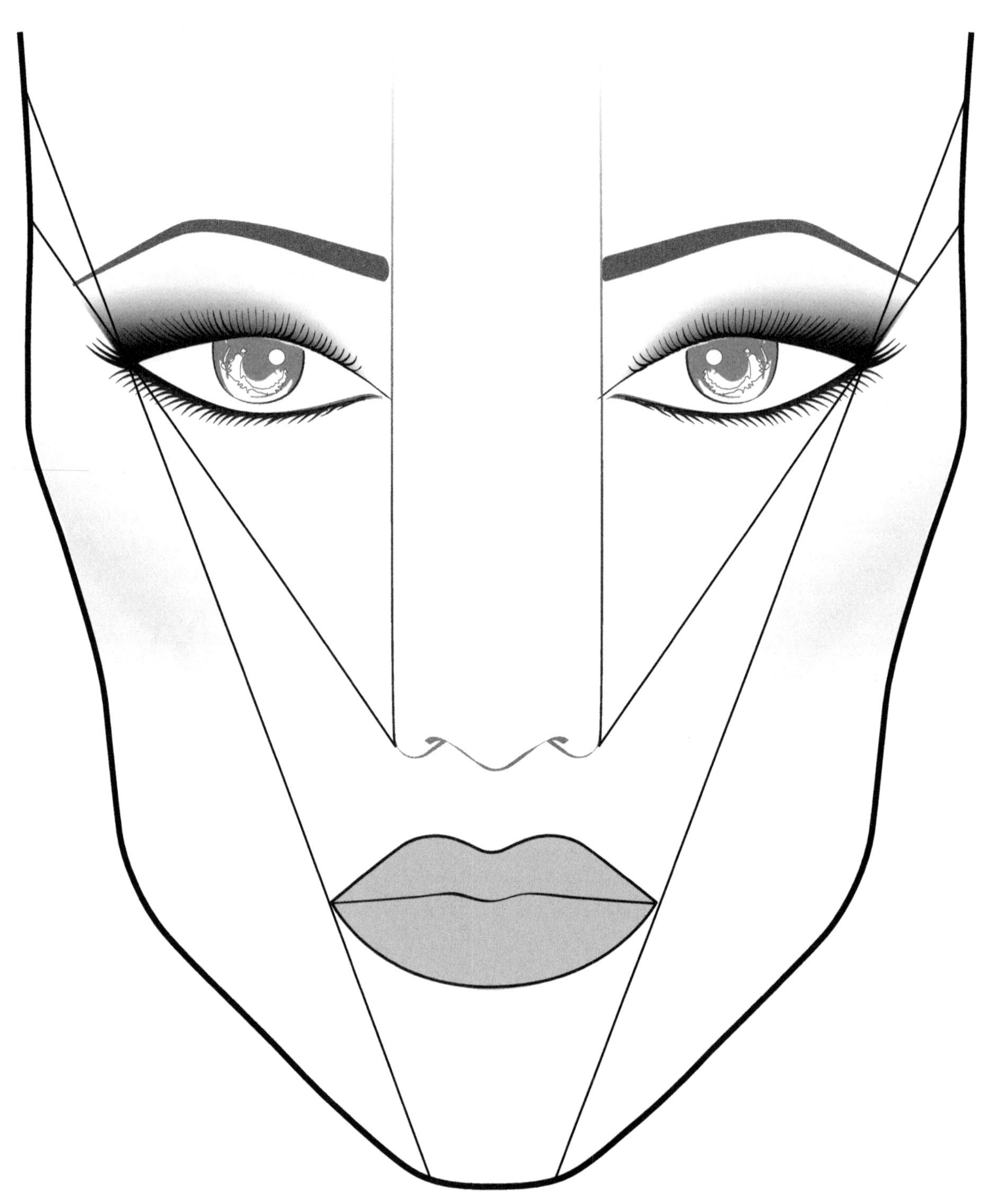

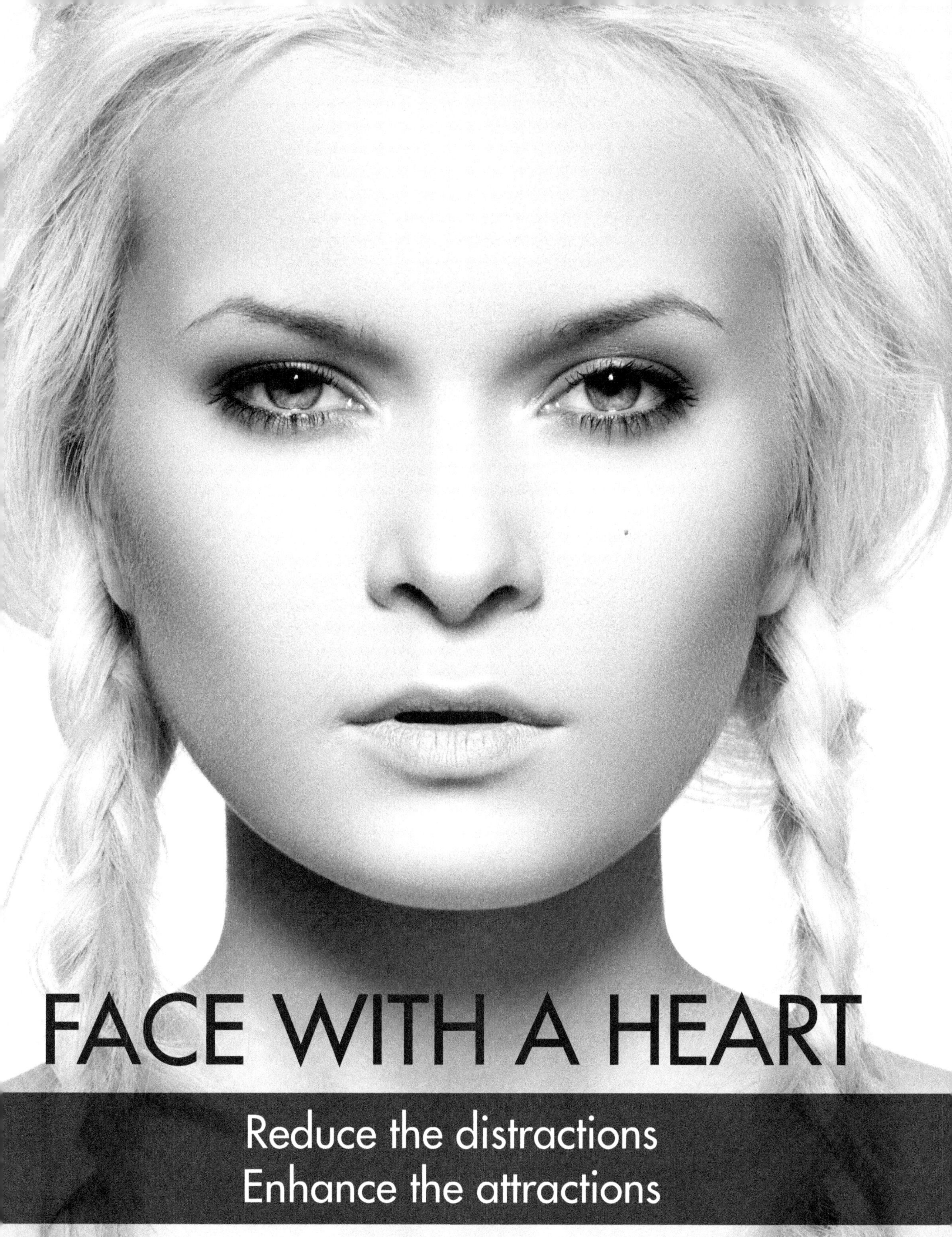
FACE WITH A HEART
Reduce the distractions
Enhance the attractions

MAKEUP STATION

The better the environment for applying makeup, the more successful the makeup application. Always keep these tips in mind when applying makeup.

Work with front light, not overhead light. Front light (light in front of you) evenly illuminates all the features simultaneously. Overhead light creates downward shadows which conflict with makeup application.

If doing makeup on someone else, step back three feet from time to time, just as an artist does with a painting, to make sure the artistry is in balance. This three foot rule shows us how the makeup will appear in public. If your makeup looks correct from three feet away, then move on to the next step of your application. If not, make the corrections necessary, check it again from three feet away, then move on.

It is ideal when applying makeup to yourself to have two mirrors; one close in order to apply makeup specifically and one three feet away to see the specific application in perspective to the rest of the face.

Makeup Brushes

Since this book focuses solely on the *Face with a Heart* method, a discussion of brushes is appropriate before beginning the explanation of the application. There are specific brushes for each step in the process. The proper use of brushes takes makeup application from the general to the specific. When makeup is applied specifically, application becomes easier and the desired results are consistently achieved. In order to achieve this specificity of application, the makeup brush design must become more specific as well.

The brush market has changed in recent years. In the past, natural hair was the best bristle (except for wet/cream products). Due to the advancements made in synthetic/nylon bristles, every brush now has the option of being either a natural or synthetic bristle. The advantage of a synthetic bristle is that it may be used with any product formula, wet or dry. Natural hair bristles may only be used with dry products. Natural hair bristles will absorb the oils from a wet product and will become heavy and limp, rendering the natural hair brush useless. Regardless of the bristle type preferred, it is imperative that specific brushes are used for specific application techniques. Specific brushes will guide the artist to the most successful application.

Listed below are the specific brushes used for the *Face with a Heart* method of application.

1. **Eyebrow brush** (Eyes: Step 1)
   A very thin and angled edge brush is best to apply a thin crisp line that is then easily blended with the thin slanted edge of the brush tip. This also works for blending pencil applications. A clean mascara-like brush is ideal for further softening and blending of application if needed.

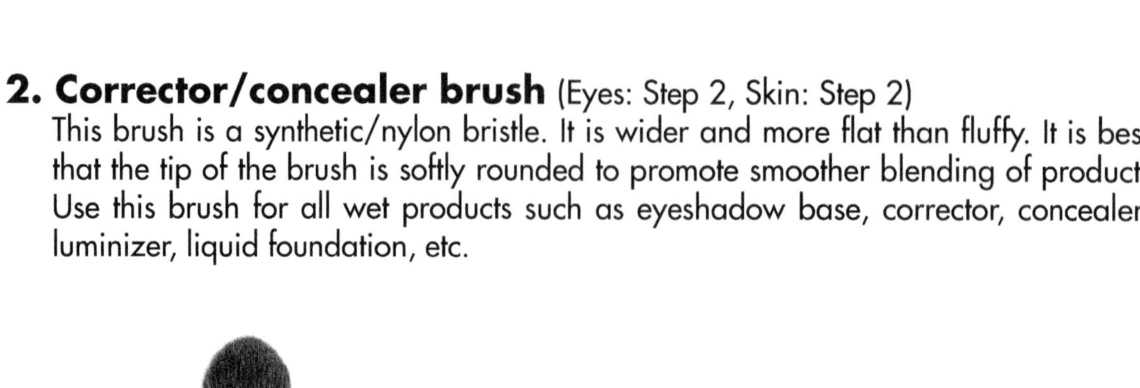

2. Corrector/concealer brush (Eyes: Step 2, Skin: Step 2)

This brush is a synthetic/nylon bristle. It is wider and more flat than fluffy. It is best that the tip of the brush is softly rounded to promote smoother blending of product. Use this brush for all wet products such as eyeshadow base, corrector, concealer, luminizer, liquid foundation, etc.

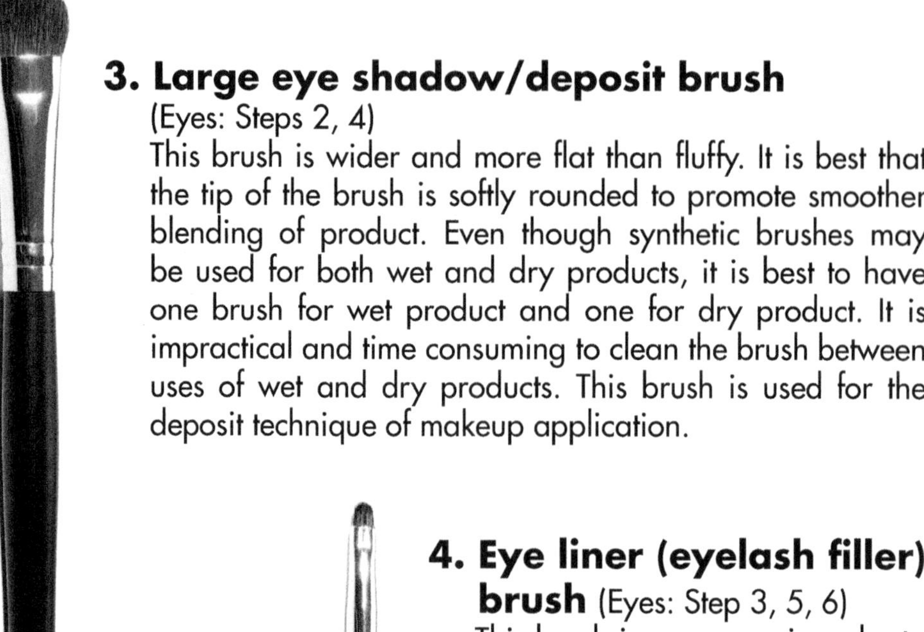

3. Large eye shadow/deposit brush

(Eyes: Steps 2, 4)

This brush is wider and more flat than fluffy. It is best that the tip of the brush is softly rounded to promote smoother blending of product. Even though synthetic brushes may be used for both wet and dry products, it is best to have one brush for wet product and one for dry product. It is impractical and time consuming to clean the brush between uses of wet and dry products. This brush is used for the deposit technique of makeup application.

4. Eye liner (eyelash filler) brush (Eyes: Step 3, 5, 6)

This brush is necessary in order to achieve the lash filler and fuzzy liner effects shown in this book. The bristles on the brush are extremely short and the tip is rounded.

5. Eye shadow crease/contour brush (Eyes: Step 4)

This brush is often referred to as a squirrel tail brush, not because it is made with squirrel hair, but because it resembles the tapered shape of a squirrel's tail. The purpose of this brush is to apply and blend eye shadow into the crease of the eye. It is most important that the tip of the brush fit snugly in the crease of the eye and be neither too stiff nor too soft. The brush should be able to apply and blend the eye shadow without poking the eye, but at the same time not lay flat when applying pressure. The size of the brush may vary depending on the shape and size of the model's eye.

6. Bullet brush (Eyes: Steps 4, 7)

This brush is an extremely versatile brush given its simple design. The bullet brush bristles mimic the tip of a pointy bullet. This brush is used for depositing shadow into small areas as well as creating the modern contour. The *Face with a Heart* method uses both the sides and tip of this brush for application.

7. Foundation brush

(Skin: Steps 1, 3)

A larger and slightly softer version of the corrector/concealer brush, the foundation brush is used to apply facial primer, foundation, luminizer, etc. It is vital that the tip of this brush be rounded and feathery soft to achieve the smoothest application possible.

8. Powder brush (Skin: Step 4)
This brush is a large, soft, and evenly beveled brush used to apply and smooth powder on the skin. The *Face with a Heart* method uses both the sides and tip of this brush for application.

9. Lip brush (Lips: Steps 2, 3)
Smaller in width yet slightly long bristled; the lip brush is used to create a variety of looks for the lips. A retractable brush is handy for at-home as well as touch-up applications.

10. Face contour brush
(Cheeks: Step 1)
This brush resembles a smaller and flatter powder brush with a slightly angled tip. The size of this brush will vary from model to model as there is a wide range of face sizes.

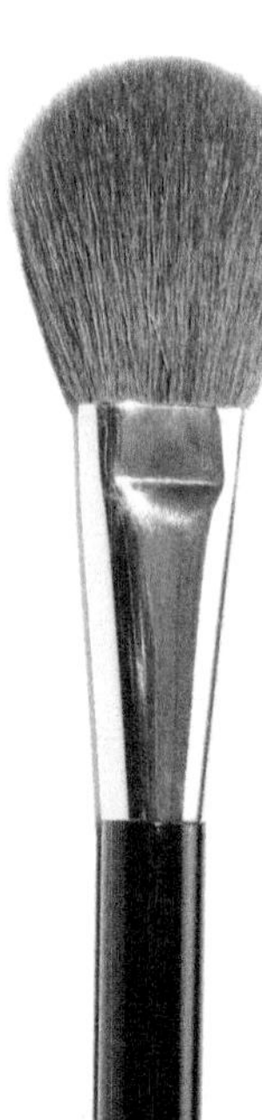

11. Blush brush
(Cheeks: Steps 1, 2)
The blush brush is a smaller version of the powder brush in every way. The tip should be no larger than the apple of the cheek of the model.

Face with a Heart Authentic Beauty Makeup

Proper Order of Makeup Application

The order of application is more important than including every step. Use this as a baseline from which to build upon any authentic makeup look. Follow the suggested order of application to achieve maximum results with minimum repair/cleaning-up time.

Eyes

1. Eye brows *
2. Eye shadow base plus powder *
3. Lash filler (upper lash bed eye liner) with waterproof liner *
4. Eye shadow- Classic Contour method
   - Light luminous shadow on lid.
   - Darker shadow in crease.
   - Neutral matte or soft shimmer shadow under eyebrow
5. Fuzzy liner (bottom lash bed eyeliner-optional)
6. Wedge eyeliner. Also acts as cat eye preparation
7. Modern contour method.
   - Wedge shadow over wedge eyeliner.
   - Blend upper border to a blur
8. Clean up under eye with cleanser and cotton swab. *

Skin

1. Apply primer to re-texturize skin and maintain a long lasting foundation finish.
2. Neutralize distractions with corrector/ concealer.* Distractions may include: darkness, redness, and shadows.

   - **Pink** corrector for medium to light skin tones. Corrects darkness and brightens.
   - **Yellow Orange** corrector for medium to dark skin tones. Corrects darkness and brightens.
   - **Green** corrector for redness, focusing on interior of heart only.

Skin tone concealer to lighten where any shadow may fall and tough-to-cover blemishes and dark spots.

3. Foundation *
4. Powder *

Lips

1. Liner
2. Lip color * #
3. Lip gloss * #

Cheeks

1. Facial contour
2. Blush *
3. Highlight
4. Final powder

Mascara

Apply last-Bambi Style *

** Use only these steps only for a quick and basic look.*
 # Use one or the other or both.

Most people apply foundation first, and then move on to the features of the face (eyes, lips, cheeks).

With *Face with a Heart* application of beauty makeup, eye makeup is applied first to prevent the eye makeup application from falling down on to an otherwise flawless skin.

Also, applying eye makeup first provides the makeup artist the opportunity to trim, sharpen, and shape the eye makeup application with the foundation products.

Following the *Face with a Heart* method of eye makeup application leads to a natural progression of application that takes the look from the natural to the balanced to the dramatic. The progression demonstrated here maximizes the heart of the face and works with the widest age and feature range.

The same steps are taken with every application, and each step builds upon the last to create this effect. The intensity of the look is dictated by the point in the process that the application stops. In other words, to achieve a dramatic look, it is necessary to complete the natural and balanced steps before achieving the dramatic look.

Eyes

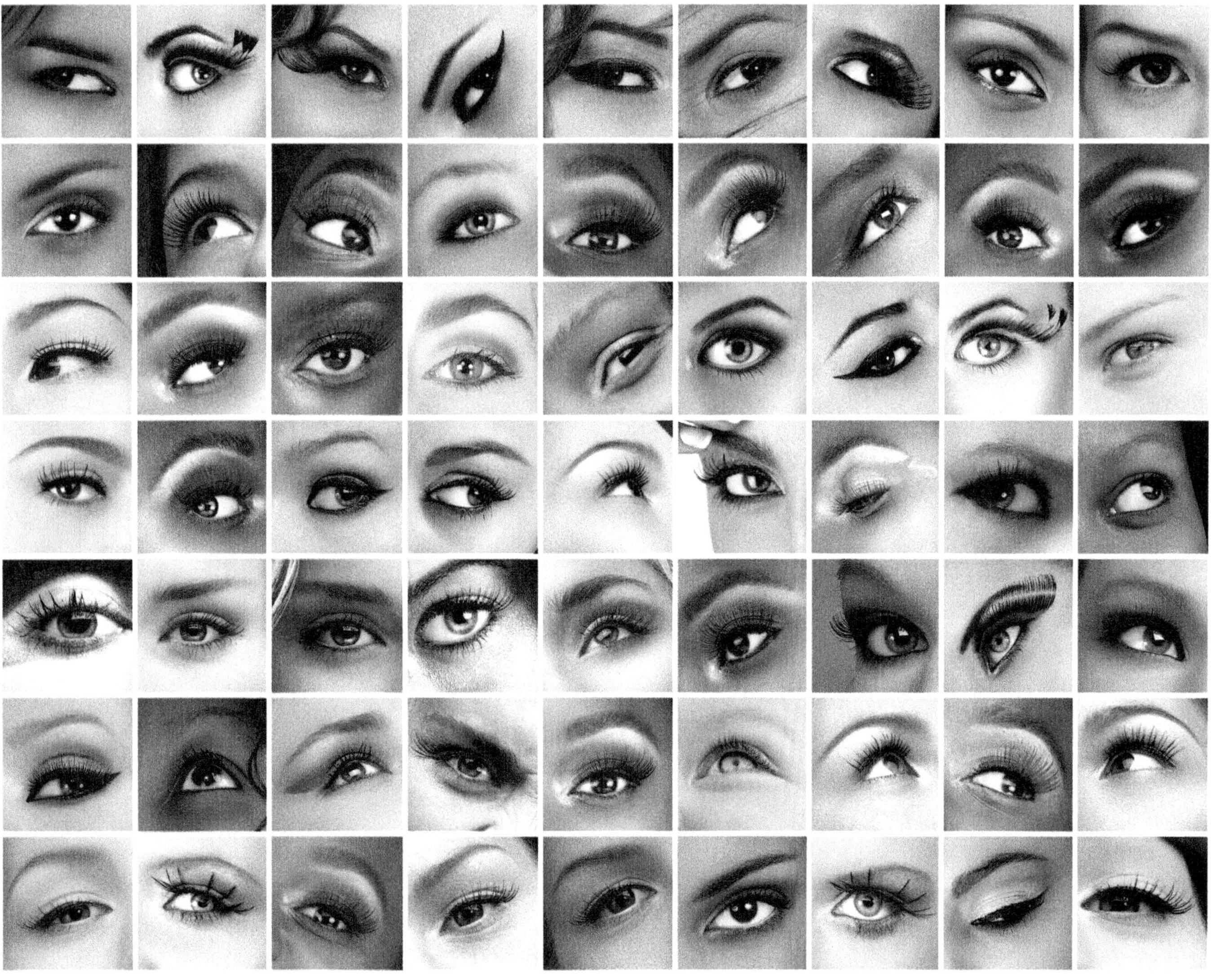

Step 1- Brows

Why:

The first thing done to the face is the most important because it establishes the placement of the remaining product. Eyebrows serve a variety of beauty makeup purposes:

- They balance and bring into symmetry the left and right side of the face. They act as the grand equalizer of sometimes otherwise asymmetrical face shapes.
- They create the top of the literal heart shape of the face
- They establish the 'world of the eye' and the placement and reason for all eye makeup.
- They support the gentle upward-outward energy of the vault of the face.

How:

The trick with eyebrows is to work within the brows that exist while maximizing their ability to frame and open the eye.

1. Establish the beginning of the brow (the side closest to the nose) by holding a thin brush handle from the nose flare past the inner corner of the eye. Make a small dot at the base of the lower edge of the eyebrow to mark the starting spot.

2. Establish outer corner of eyebrow by holding a thin brush handle from the nose flare past the outer corner of the eye. Make a dot at the outer top of the brow to define the finish point.

3.
Establish the height of the arch by holding a thin brush handle from the nose flare through the center of the iris and just to the outside of the pupil. Make a dot at the top of the eyebrow where the brush handle falls

4. There are now three dots on the brow that need to be joined with two straight lines.

5.Using an eyebrow brush with hair colored powder or a brow pencil, connect the three dots. Match the model's head hair color as closely as possible. Only blondes look natural with a darker brow color as many blondes have a naturally darker brow.

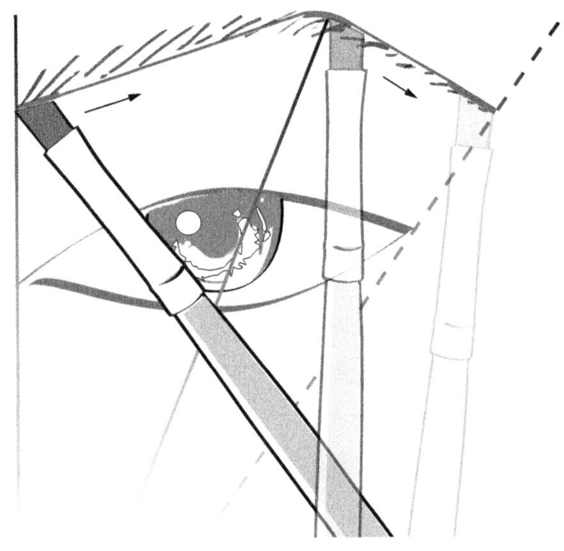

6.Starting from the inner corner, fluff the color application upwards while moving out along the brow. This will create an automatic tapered effect to the brow: thickest on the inner corner and thinnest on the outer corner.

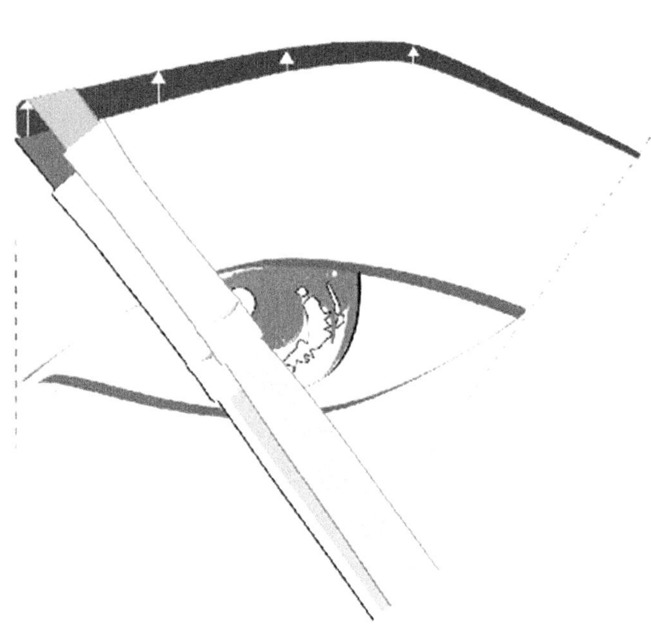

7. Only fluff up the color application to the peak of the arch of the eyebrow. Allow the outer half of the brow to remain thin to the end. This will create the illusion of a perfectly tapered brow.

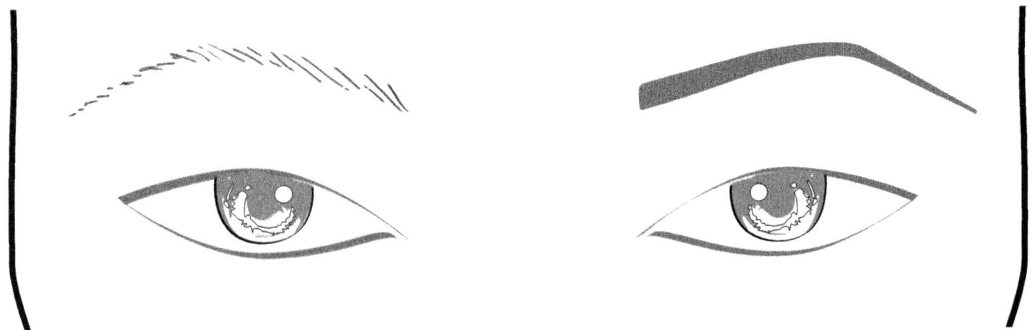

Stand 3 feet back from the mirror to assess the application and make any adjustments or fine tuning that may be required.

For longer lasting holding power, brush a clear mascara through the eyebrow brushing mostly up then slightly out to hold the hairs in a perfect outward cascade effect.

Step 2- Eye shadow base/corrector/primer

Why:

Before applying any makeup to the skin, it is important to prep the area to maximize the efficacy and longevity of the eye makeup. The correct eye shadow base provides this service.

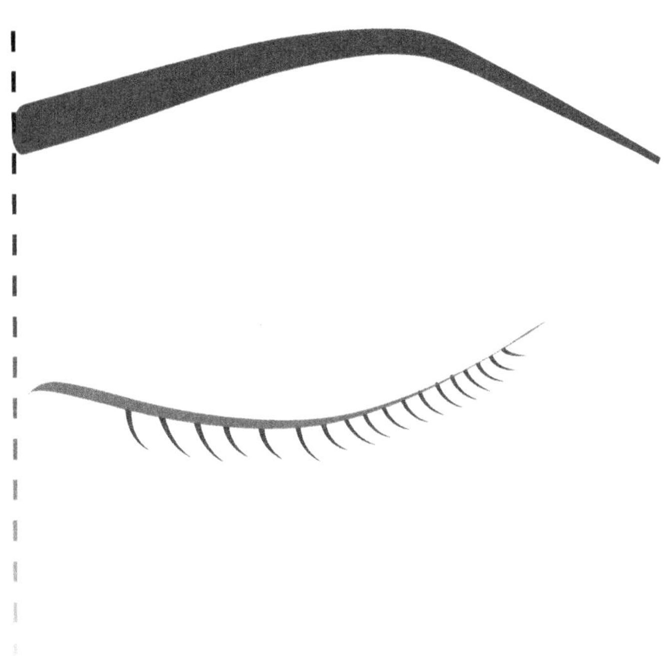

When it comes to wearing eye makeup well, there are some natural pitfalls:

- Natural eyelid discoloration can alter the desired color effect
- Constant movement of the eye (blinking) creates creasing of eye makeup
- Natural skin oils can dissolve/crease the eye makeup

Eye shadow base is applied to minimize all of these pitfalls.

The purpose of eye shadow base is to:

- Neutralize discoloration of the eyelid
- Create a brighter appearance to the eyelid
- Support and maintain the true color of the eye makeup
- Prevent creasing, fading of eye makeup

There are many types of eye shadow base (also known as primers) on the market, but the best eye shadow base (also known as primers) on the market, but the best eye shadow base is one that accomplishes all of the above in one product.

How:

Using a corrector/concealer brush, apply the eye shadow base/primer across the entire world of the eye area keeping these points in mind:

a. Use very little product at a time and learn to layer up the coverage desired, not spread the product down to the thinness desired.

b. Apply more product where the lid is darker (usually closer to the lash line)

c. Sweep the corrector/concealer brush horizontally left and right to achieve an even disbursement of product.

d. Use the tip of the brush to apply along the under side of the eyebrow to create the crispest underside to the eye brow possible

e. Apply until the eye area is completely neutralized and stop before the product begins to build up and become apparent on the eye.

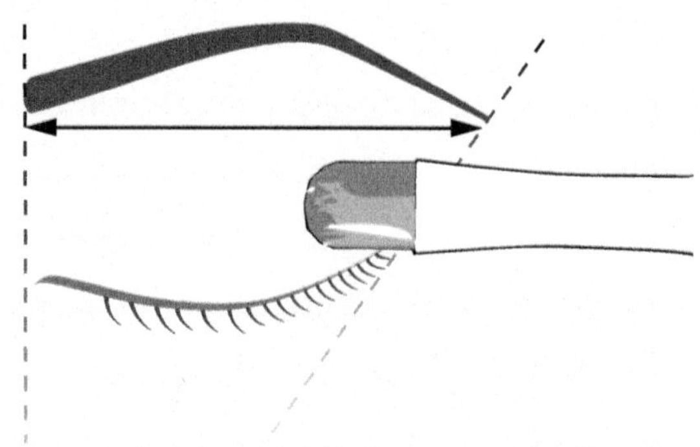

Deposit Technique

Deposit is a technique for applying color to the face that gives the artist maximum control. Deposit a thin layer of translucent pressed powder appropriate for the skin tone of the model over the whole eye area where eye shadow base has been applied.

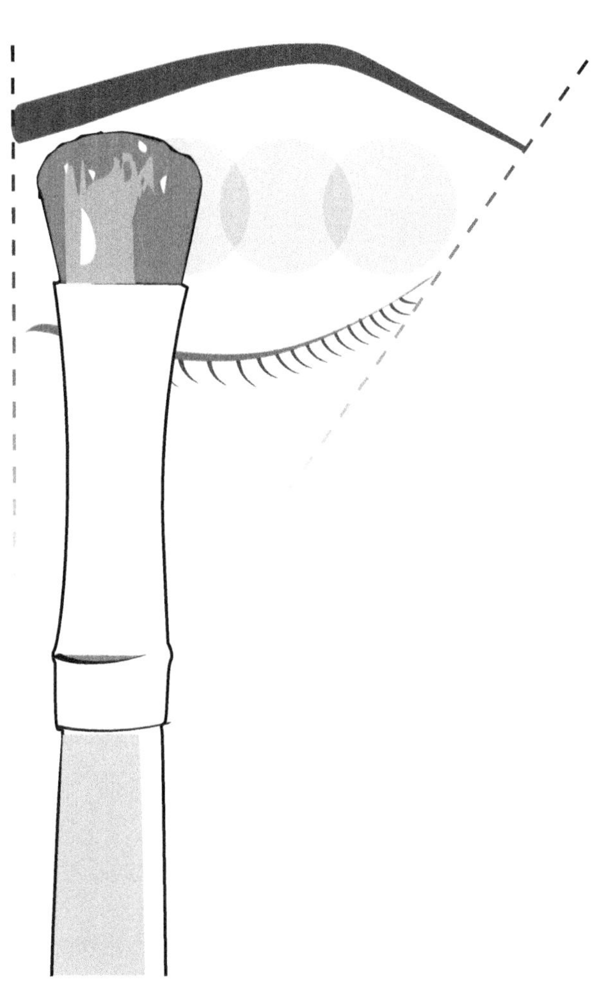

Deposit Technique

1. Use a large eye shadow/deposit brush.

2. Press the two flat sides of the deposit brush into the powder to fill up the sides of the brush with product. It may help to wiggle the brush a little while the sides of the brush are in the product. Do not swirl the brush into the product. It causes waste, a mess and does not effectively put product on the brush.

3. Flick off any excess product from the deposit brush. This is done by flicking a free finger on the handle of the brush (not easy) or tapping the brush handle on your free hand.

4. Now gently yet firmly press the side of the deposit brush onto the eye area. Repeat this until the entire world of the eye has been set with powder.

5. When one side of the deposit brush runs out of product, flip it over and use the other side. This way you can set both eyes with one brushful of powder.

The deposit technique is always used when applying and intensifying the application on the non-crease part of the eye. It allows you to layer the product smoothly and evenly onto the skin, always building up the look, never rubbing down.

Step 3- Lash filler (upper lash bed eye liner)

Why:

To capture the most authentic shape of every eye.

Regardless of age, the lash line (the line where your eyelashes either grow or use to grow) captures absolutely the true shape of the eye. Even as skin matures and the skin around the eye may change dramatically, the lash line shape remains intact. By enhancing the lash line, the eye shape retains its eternal (youthful) shape and is the most natural looking shape to the observer.

How:

This technique is the truest way to capture the natural shape of every eye.

It is best to use waterproof/non-liquid eye liner for this step. Waterproof so it doesn't run and non-liquid because the slow-drying nature of a liquid liner doesn't lend itself well to this technique.
The preferred liner is waterproof gel eye liner with a brush or a high quality waterproof pencil.

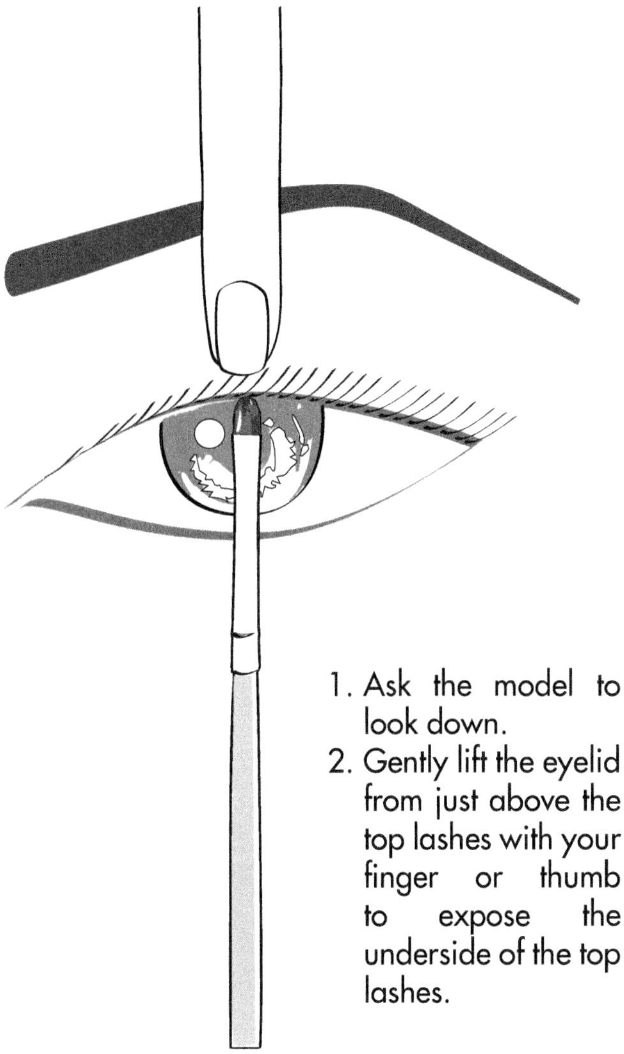

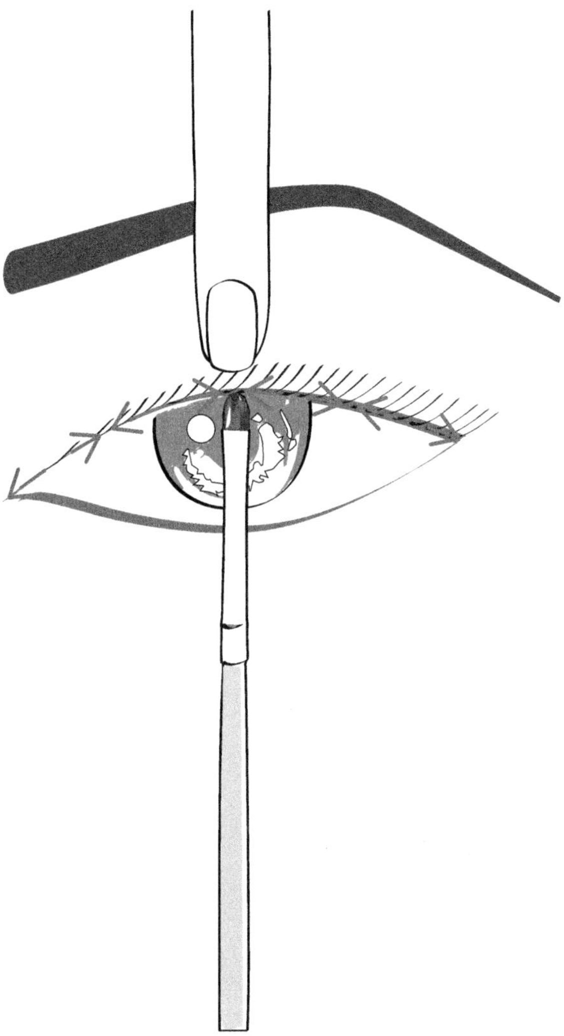

1. Ask the model to look down.
2. Gently lift the eyelid from just above the top lashes with your finger or thumb to expose the underside of the top lashes.
3. With a sketching motion, fill in the entire underside of the top lash bed area with the lash filler (upper lash bed eyeliner) brush. Avoid drawing a line. Instead work the liner into the lashes with a back and forth sketching motion (liner will get into the base of the top lash hairs and that is ok).
4. The rule is to fill in everywhere where lashes grow. To make the eyes look their biggest, take this lash liner all the way into the inner corner of the eye. The longer the line the bigger the width and lift of the eye. (Exception to the rule: Not suggested to go to the far inner corner of the eyes for very close-set eyes as it will make them appear more close-set).
5. Always err on the side of making the lashes more prominent from the pupil of the eyes outward to open up the outer corner of the eyes.

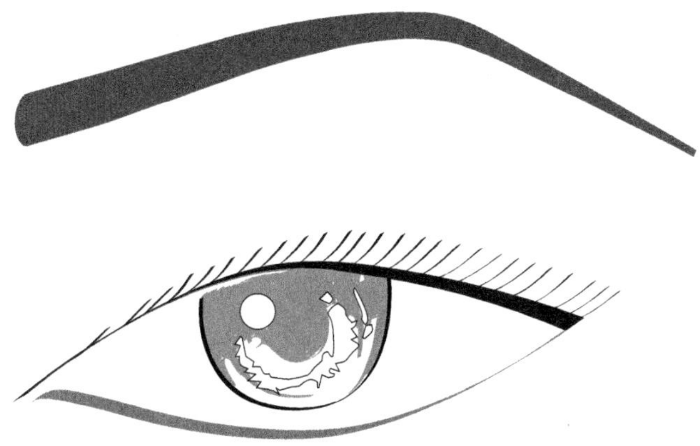

Step 4- Eye Shadow: Classic contour method

Why:

To maximize shape, volume, depth, and color of the eye.

Eye shadow has an infinite level of possibilities, so it is best to understand the principles of eye shadow which will help create the most authentic shape of any eye.

Principles of eye shadow:

- Lighter shades bring shape forward
- Darker shades sink shapes deeper back (recede)
- Shimmer reflects light and pulls focus to it and may bring shape forward
- Matte absorbs light and diminishes reflection and may sink shape deeper back.

Eye shadow is the best way to maximize the shape of your eyelid.

The two primary methods of eye shadow application are Classic Contour and Modern Contour. The second method may be an extension of the first, or it may be used alone. There is also a bridge between the two looks called wedge eye liner. The wedge eye liner is an option that may be used with either of these looks. Any liner technique, such as the wedge eye liner, that is designed to alter the shape of the authentic eye line, is also known as an art liner.

How:

There are three basic parts of an eyelid that separate and define the shape of the eye.
They are:

- Ball
- Brow
- Crease

The ball of the eye is the skin that has the eyeball immediately underneath it when the eyes are closed.

The brow is any part under the eyebrow that has bone underneath it.

The crease, and this is important, is the area under the curvature of the brow bone where it meets the ball of the eye. It is a sunken groove that is highly rounded as the eye sockets are highly rounded. Think of this crease as a groove or track where your contour brush is designed to slip into and follow the natural curvature of the eye socket where it meets the eyeball.

When applying eye shadow (and most color for that matter) always add and buildup to the desired effect. Try to avoid getting too much of anything on the face and having to rub it down or off. That is the essence of makeup gone wrong. As long as the intensity is always building up away from the face, the makeup appears connected to the person wearing it and gives the greatest control when applying any look.

Classic Contour Method of Application

Ball of the eye

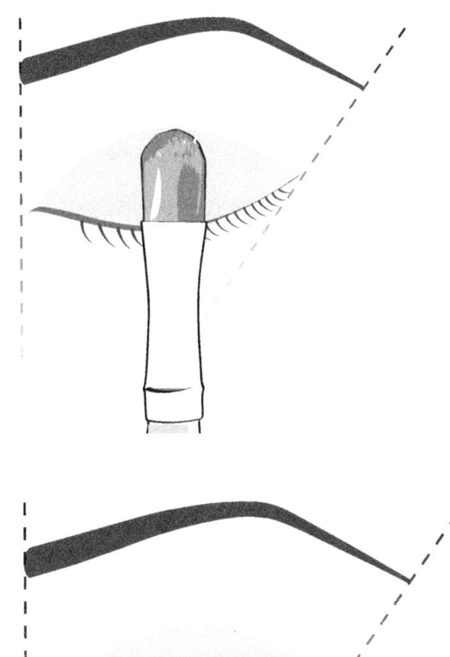

1. Select three shades of eye shadow: Light, Light-medium, and medium to dark.

2. Using the deposit method and the large eye shadow/deposit brush, deposit the light or medium-light shadow on the ball of the eye. Build up the color saturation by depositing more layers of the eye shadow until the desired saturation of pigment is achieved. It is better to deposit than rub the eye shadow on the lid. Rubbing tends to unevenly distribute the shadow and makes a bigger spill outside the intended target.

3. 'The end result is a high-lighted ball of the eye that draws attraction to it because of its lightness. If using a satin/shimmer finish eye shadow, the reflection of light from the eyeshadow increases the attraction to the ball of the eye. There is concern among more mature people to stay away from shadow with any shimmer. The ball of the eye is the one place where a satin-like shimmer shadow works on any eye.

Crease of the eye

This step is the key element to the Classic Contour look. The objective is to add depth to the area where shadow naturally falls on the eye, in the crease. By deepening the effect of the shadow, the eye becomes more dynamic, bigger looking, and lifts the outer corner of the eye upwards in a 45 degree angle enhancing the vault of the face.

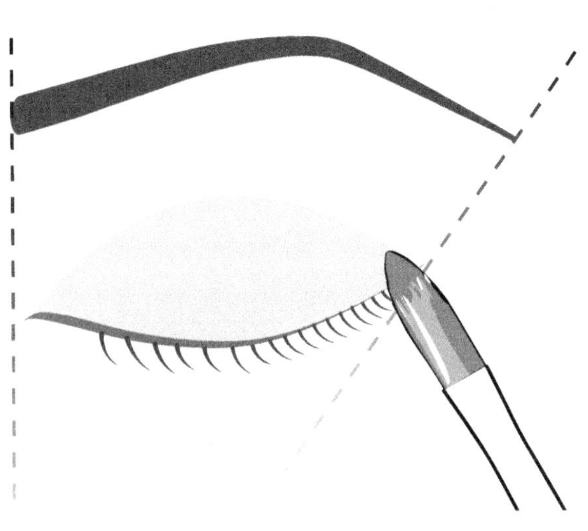

1. Select the darkest shade and dip only the very tip of the eye shadow crease/contour brush into the color. A makeup artist needs a wide variety of contour brush sizes to best fit into the crease of the model. The tip of the brush needs to snugly fit into the crease without spilling on the ball or the brow bone.

2. This next step is mandatory for creating the perfect contour successfully. Start with the tip of the eye shadow crease/contour brush perpendicular to the face in the very outer corner of the eye where the crease begins along the same line used to measure the world of the eye, namely from the nose flare to the outer corner of the eye.

3. With a single rounded stroke, circle the eye shadow crease/contour brush with the tip of the brush in the crease from the outer corner up to the center of the eye staying in the crease the entire time. Stop when the brush is directly over the pupil of the eye.

4. Now remove the eye shadow crease/contour brush from the eye and repeat step 3 over and over until there is no more product left on the brush.

5. Assess whether more color is needed in the crease. If so, repeat step 1 through 4. Continue to do this until there is enough depth of color in the outer crease of the eye.

6. Once the desired intensity is reached, put the tip of the eye shadow crease/contour brush into the crease and sweep it gently and evenly from the outer to inner corner of the crease and back again. Continue sweeping in both directions like a windshield wiper until the contour color has blended itself into the crease.

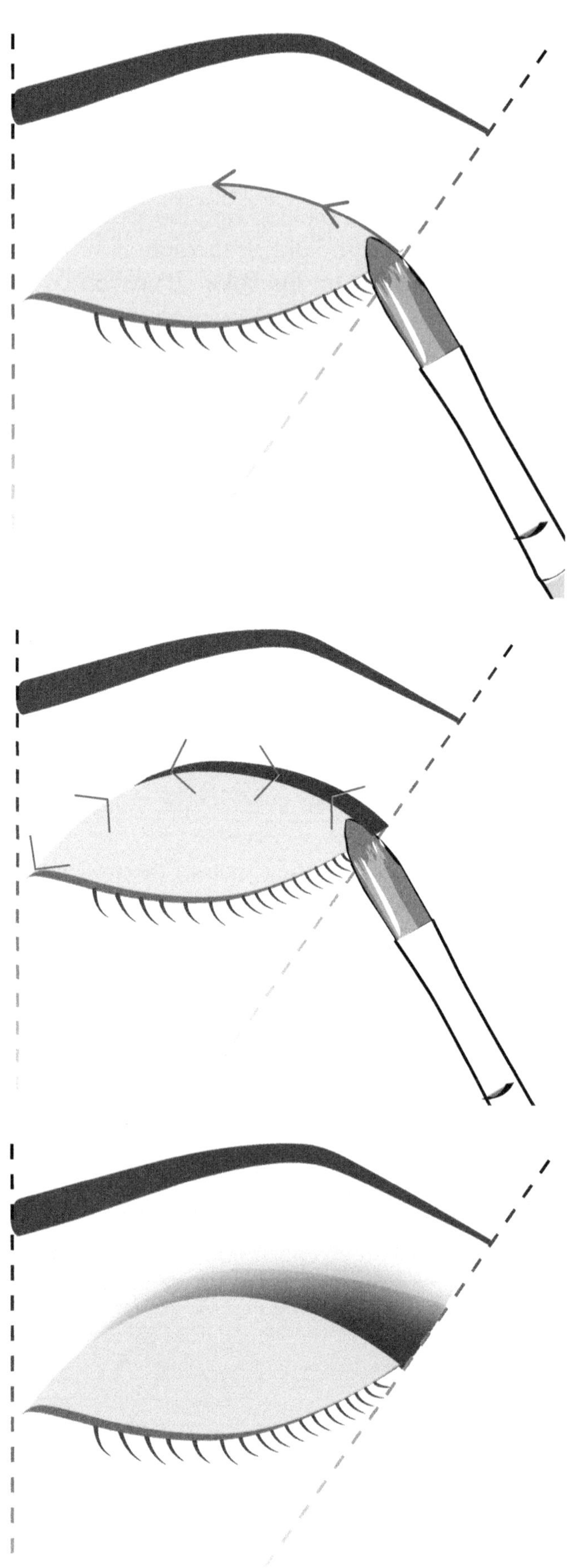

A note about blending: All shadows work differently in respect to how they blend. Try not to force, rush, or bully the color into blending. Blending takes a fair amount of patience and persistence. Shadow will blend when it is ready to and not before and rushing it will only make it worse. The darker the pigment, the more stubborn it is to blend. This is when the greatest patience and highest amount of blending is required.

Brow Bone

The area remaining above the crease is the brow bone.

1. With a bullet brush, deposit the third (and mostly neutral) color on the brow bone using the side of the brush.

2. Deposit this shadow directly under the eyebrow and along the border (not over) the crease color.

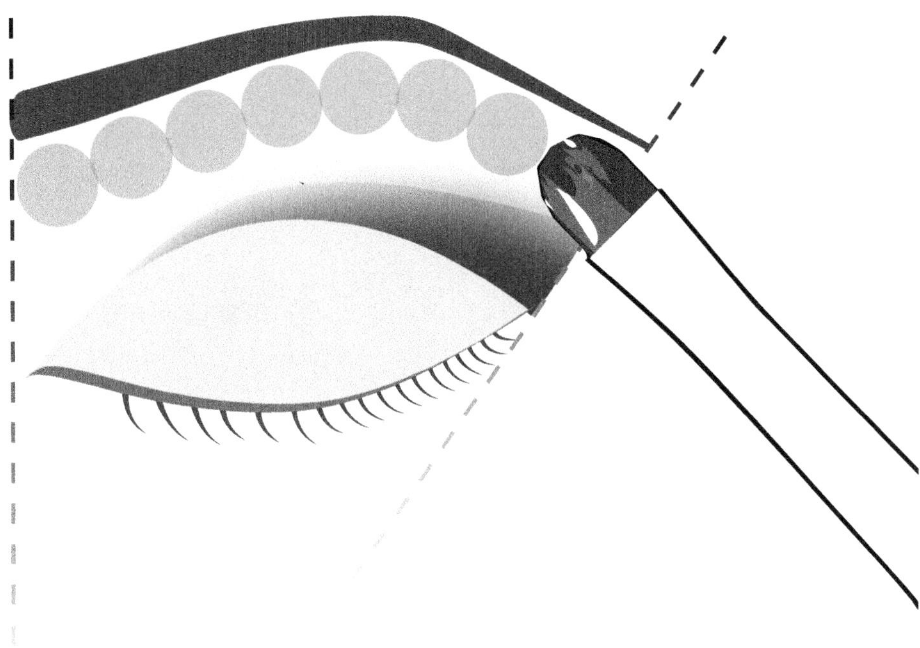

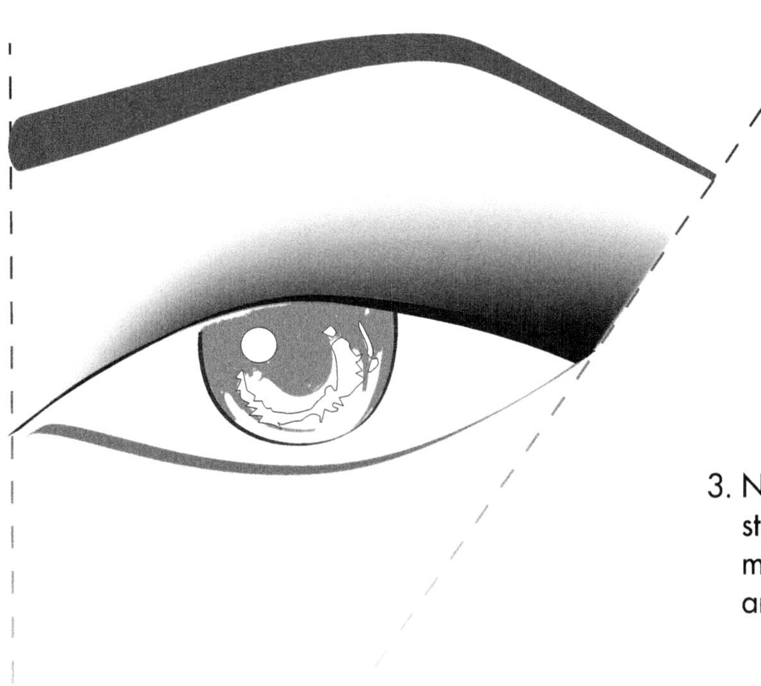

3. Now allow the tip of the bullet brush to straddle where the crease and brow color meet and gently sweep in a half circle back and forth to blend (blur) the two colors.

Without the presence of a bottom eye liner, this look reads as natural and is a great place to stop. To quickly provide a more, professional balanced look to the eye makeup, add this next step.

Step 5- Fuzzy liner

(bottom lash eye liner-optional)

Why:

To completely capture the shape of the eye, applying lash liner along the bottom lashes will serve to achieve this affect.

Although not mandatory, fuzzy liner makes a big difference in the look of the makeup. This is one of those points in the application where the next step strongly affects the intensity of the eye makeup.

For a very natural look, no need to line the bottom lashes.

For a more balanced look, it is preferred to line the bottom lashes. Fuzzy liner is a technique of application that applies the lash liner in a diffused, slightly soft focus way, and the bottom liner is half the intensity of the top liner. This way people will always look up into the eyes first, rather than at the eye liner below the eye.

How:

1. Pick a waterproof eye liner color at least half the intensity of the top lash liner, or, more softly apply the same color.

2. To expose the lashes in the best, most gentle way, gently push in right under the bottom lashes with your fingertip.

3. The bottom lashes will bow forward and down automatically. No need to pull the eye down to do this technique.

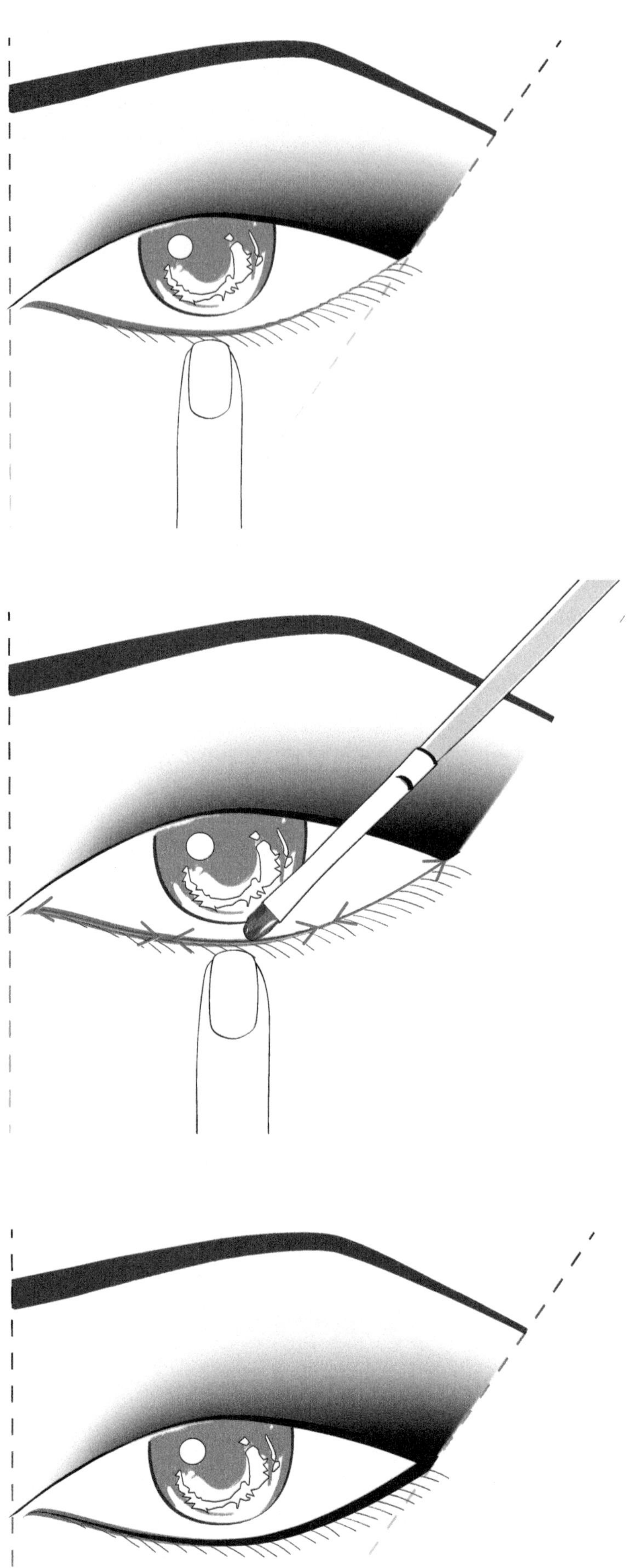

4. Working from above the bottom lash line, softly sweep the eye liner brush along the roots of the bottom lashes. The bottom line needs to appear slightly diffused (fuzzy) whereas the top eye liner (lash filler) is crisp and more defined. This will keep the focus up and into the eyes and not below the eyes.

5. Always err on the side of applying more on the outer half of the lash line (except for wide set eyes).

6. A waterproof eye liner product is best as this liner is so close to the eye. For this look, liquid liner is not suggested.

Please note: This fuzzy liner is going between the lashes and not on the wet line, the area between the eye and the lashes. Only put liner on the wet line for higher intensity makeup looks.

Step 6-
Wedge liner
(Art liner)

Why:

To reshape the top eye line to create an altered version of the eye.

Art liner is what takes the eye shape one is born with and transcends it to the shape we want it to be.

The difference between lash filler and art liner is that while lash filler fully enhances the natural shape of the eye, art eye liner creates the eye shape we want it to be.

For beauty makeup purposes, create an eye shape that supports all the basic principles of beauty makeup including:

- Heart of the face
- Vault of the face
- World of the eye
- Sweet spot of the eye

As with eye shadow, there are a limitless variety of application techniques for art liner. For the purposes of achieving the authentic beauty makeup, the wedge liner is the best technique to support the *Face with a Heart.*

Once the wedge liner is applied, the look begins to slide into a more dramatic look.

How:

It is required that the lash filler step has been applied. The next step is to connect the wedge liner to the lash filler to open and vault the eye.

For this technique, focus on the sweet spot of the eye.

When the liner from the pupil of the eye out to the corner of the eye is enhanced, maximum vault and lift of the eye is achieved.

When the eye is open, the natural top lash line ascends from the inner corner of the eye to the center of the eye, just over the pupil of the eye. From there the top natural lash line descends to the outer corner of the eye.

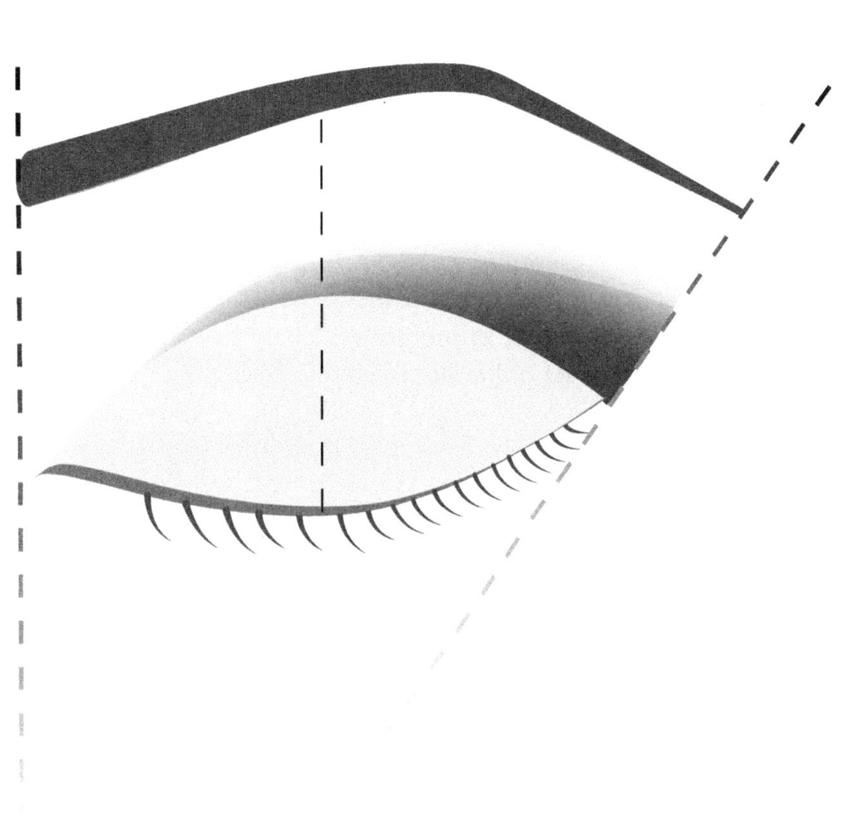

The wedge liner greatly diminishes or eliminates the descent of the lash line so the eye climbs outward and upward from the center of the eye out. Simply put, it lifts the eye without the appearance of exaggerated makeup.

For this application, use the liner formula (gel, pencil, felt tip, liquid, etc.) which gives the artist the greatest control. This may vary from person to person, but it is imperative to make a clean, well defined line.

1. Start from the outer corner of the top lash line and fill in the top lash line to the center of the eye. In essence it is lash filler working from above the lash line rather than below as in the previous lash filler application. This is to give the outer lash line more fullness.

2. Now repeat this application only start a little higher in the outer corner of the eye and draw a straight line into the center of the eye.

3. Where the line finishes over the center of the eye, it needs to dive back into the lash line to create a seamless connection between art line and lash line.

4. Now repeat the last step again starting a little higher than before, lining inwards and always ending up in the exact same spot over the center of the eye.

5. Use the outer edge of the "world of the eye" as the starting point to increase the intensity (thickness) of the liner.

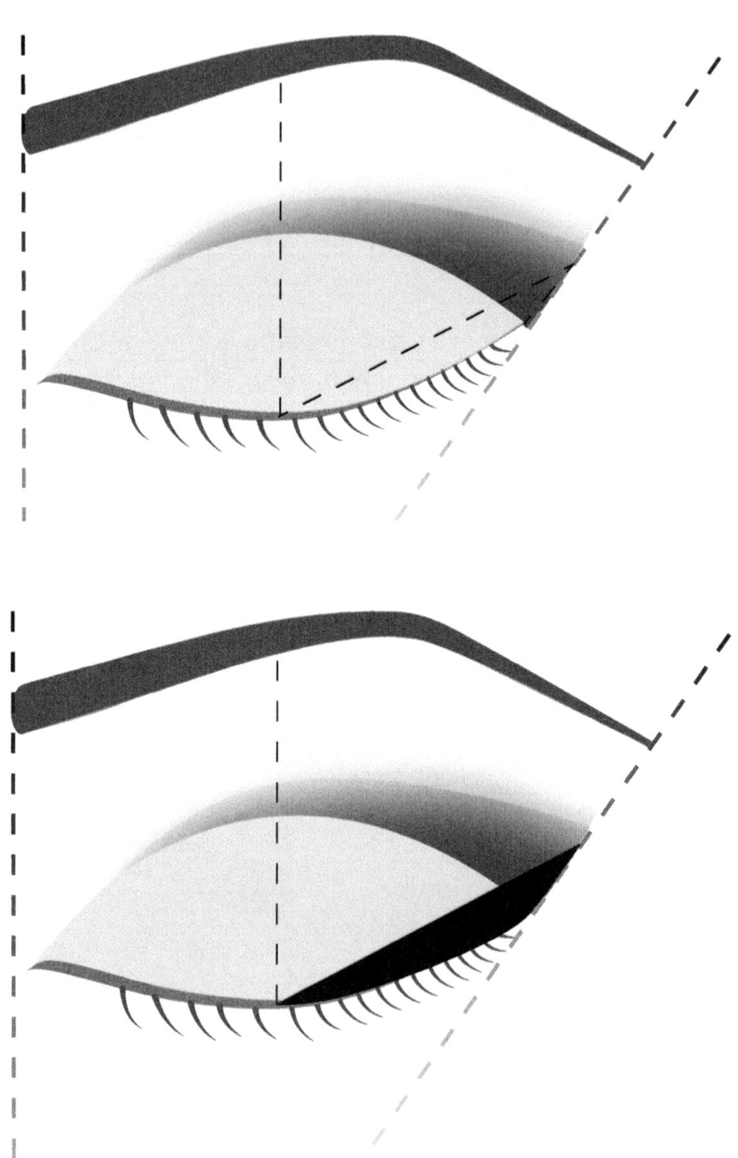

Please note: this is really hard to do on yourself. Most people naturally prefer to start from the center of the eye and apply outward to the corner. This is ok, not preferred, but ok. Because this technique is challenging, adjust how you apply the liner to best suit the greatest ease of application.

Ultimately, the goal is to achieve the same effect regardless of the application method.
This technique is also the base for a "cat eye" liner. Only with a cat eye the outer border of the world of the eye breaks to draw focus more to the makeup than the eye. This is a trend look and, not part of the *Face with a Heart* look.

Step 7- Eye shadow: Modern contour

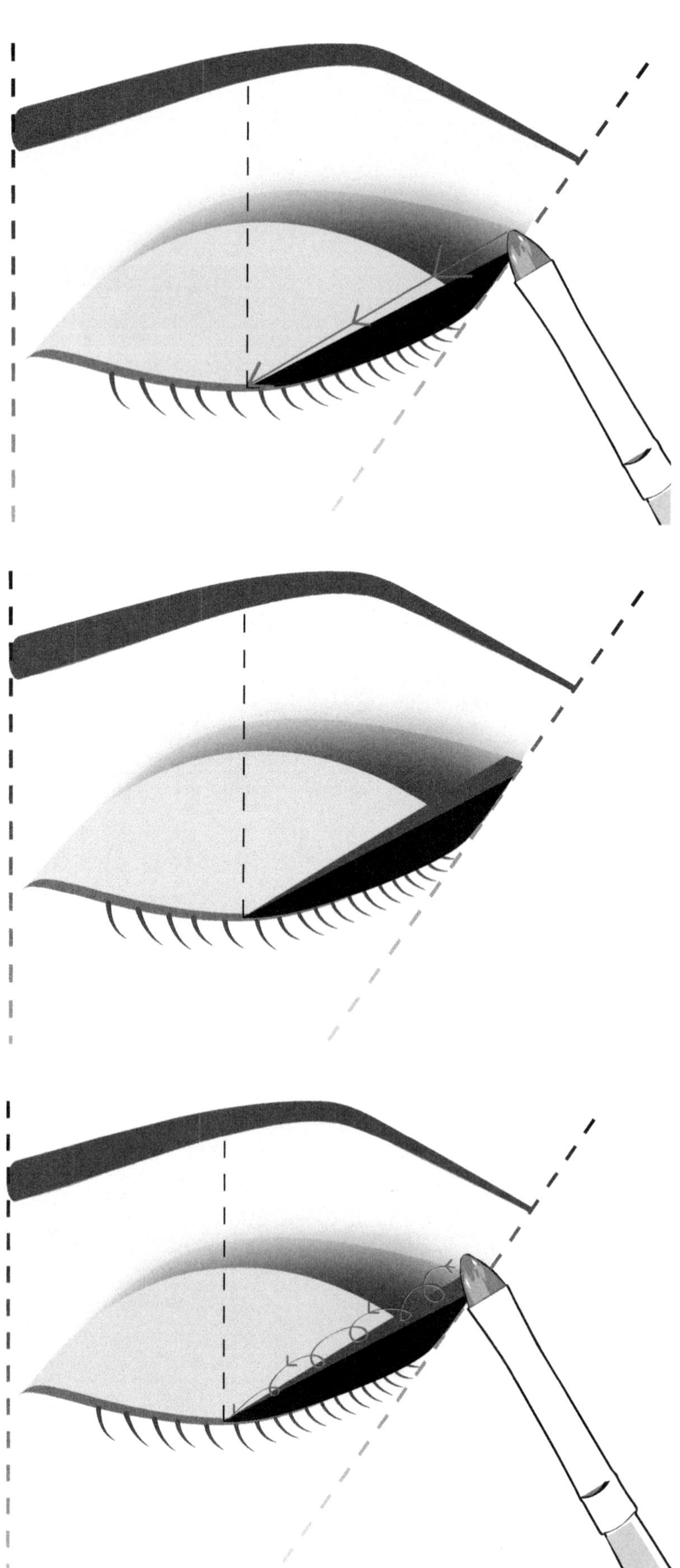

Why:

The modern contour may be used in addition to or as an alternative to the classic contour.
It provides more color weight to the outer corner of the eye.
The affect of this technique lends itself to opening the eyes outward and gently upwards.
Though beautiful on everyone, it is very effective on a mature eyelid that has lost some of its visible eye crease due to loss of elasticity in the eyelid.

It was a technique used on Marilyn Monroe often to create her trademark 'bedroom eye' look.

How:

- Using the bullet brush, brush a darker shadow from the outer corner of the eye in the crease to the center of the eyelid ending and diving into the lash line at the pupil. (Please note: this application mimics the wedge eye liner, only a thicker version).
- The shape drawn is similar to an elongated triangle or a doorstop.
- With a very small circular motion, using the side of the bullet brush, gently blur the upper descending border of the contour up and in as the brush moves towards the center of the eye at the lash line.

Watch the companion video tutorials at: http://makeupgourmet.com/thecourses/

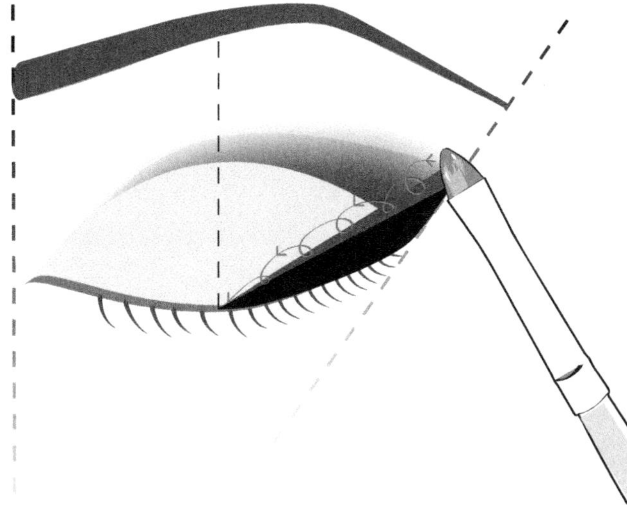

- Repeat this until the modern contour is blended to satisfaction.

Step 8: Clean-up the under-eye area

Why:

Eye makeup spills outwards in almost every direction no matter how carefully it is applied. That is why the eye makeup is applied before proceeding to the appearance of skin.

Key reasons for cleaning up now:
- Time/step saver- Wait to do all the cleaning maintenance at one time during the application rather than little fixes all along the way. This will save time and energy.

- Sharpen and crisp up the edges of the eye makeup by trimming away the unwanted spilling excess.

- Avoid all of this mess going into a perfectly prepared foundation. There is no point in doing a beautiful foundation if pigment from the eye makeup spills on top of it

- Re-moisturizes the under-eye area before the crucial correction phase of makeup for a smoother application to the delicate under-eye area.

How:

Simply saturate a cotton swab with tissue off cleanser (cleanser that doesn't require water, like Cetaphil) and wipe away all residual makeup that fell under the eye as well as outside the borders of the world of the eye.

As a precaution, wipe all the way down to the base of the nose. Pigment floats farther down than realized as eye makeup is being applied.

Use the clean side of the cotton swab to remove any excess cleanser from the face.

Skin

The goal is to make skin look like skin. The trick is to get the desired finish without the appearance of a makeup-heavy looking skin. It is easy to coat the face in makeup and achieve a flawless appearance. The problem is that the skin is no longer skin, it is a makeup delivery system.

The system shared here to achieve flawless skin-like skin is both highly objective and extremely intuitive. It is a delicate balance between the power of beauty makeup and the purpose of beauty makeup. More than with any other aspect of makeup application, respect for the face and the ability to build up to the desired affect come into play. Being insistent on technique and color choice make or break this most important part of makeup application.
Here is the approach. The skin within the heart is at a level 10 coverage (10 being the highest, keeping in mind that level 10 is different for every person and every look). Once you get to the outside of the heart, your makeup application on the skin decelerates in this order:
9-8-7-6-5-4-3-2-1 as foundation moves to the outer edges of the hairline and jawline.

The best advice is:

- Always be adding, not rubbing off.
- Apply product as thinly as possible and layer where necessary

- Only use product where you need it.
- Demand excellence of yourself, it will pay off.

Step 1- Skin primer

Why:

To maximize the smoothness of the skin and to act as a base to encourage longer and more even wear of foundation.

A silicone derivative product designed to make skin even smoother and to refine pore size are the biggest advantages of using a primer. As a rule, use primer with every makeup application as it will only enhance the appearance of the foundation and lengthen its longevity on the skin.

How:

Primer application is a good warm-up for how to apply foundation. Short of airbrush, a synthetic foundation brush is the best tool to apply foundation. There is so much to grasp here so it is important that you follow these next instructions implicitly. Appearance of skin makes or breaks an authentic makeup application. Although the concepts explained here may be challenging at first, in time they will lead to a more beautiful, longer lasting finish to foundation application.

First, for the foundation brush.

- Only use the feathery tip of the brush on the skin.
- The brush must remain fluffy in order to deliver the product at its best. If product gets deeper in the brush, the feathery tip of the brush becomes clumpy and product begins to appear to be clawing onto the skin.
- Always apply from the center of the face stroking outward on a slightly downward angle.
- Here is the most important thing to remember: The heart of the face is the focus for the appearance of skin because it contains the two main attractions on the face, the eyes and lips.
- Once the brush passes outside the heart, it is merely thinning to nothing the product left on the brush.
- Think level 10 coverage within the heart then 9-0 as the brush heads towards hairline and jawline
- The brush stroke flicks off of the jawline and never runs along it.

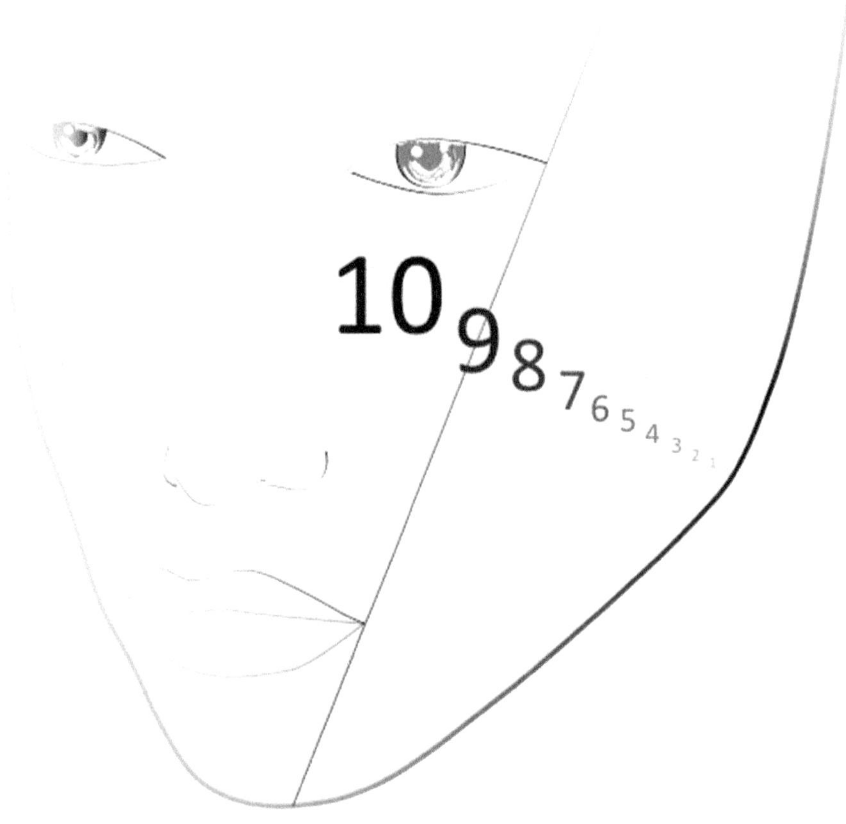

Watch the companion video tutorials at: http://makeupgourmet.com/thecourses/

Here is a suggested order of application

Divide the face right down the middle form forehead to chin

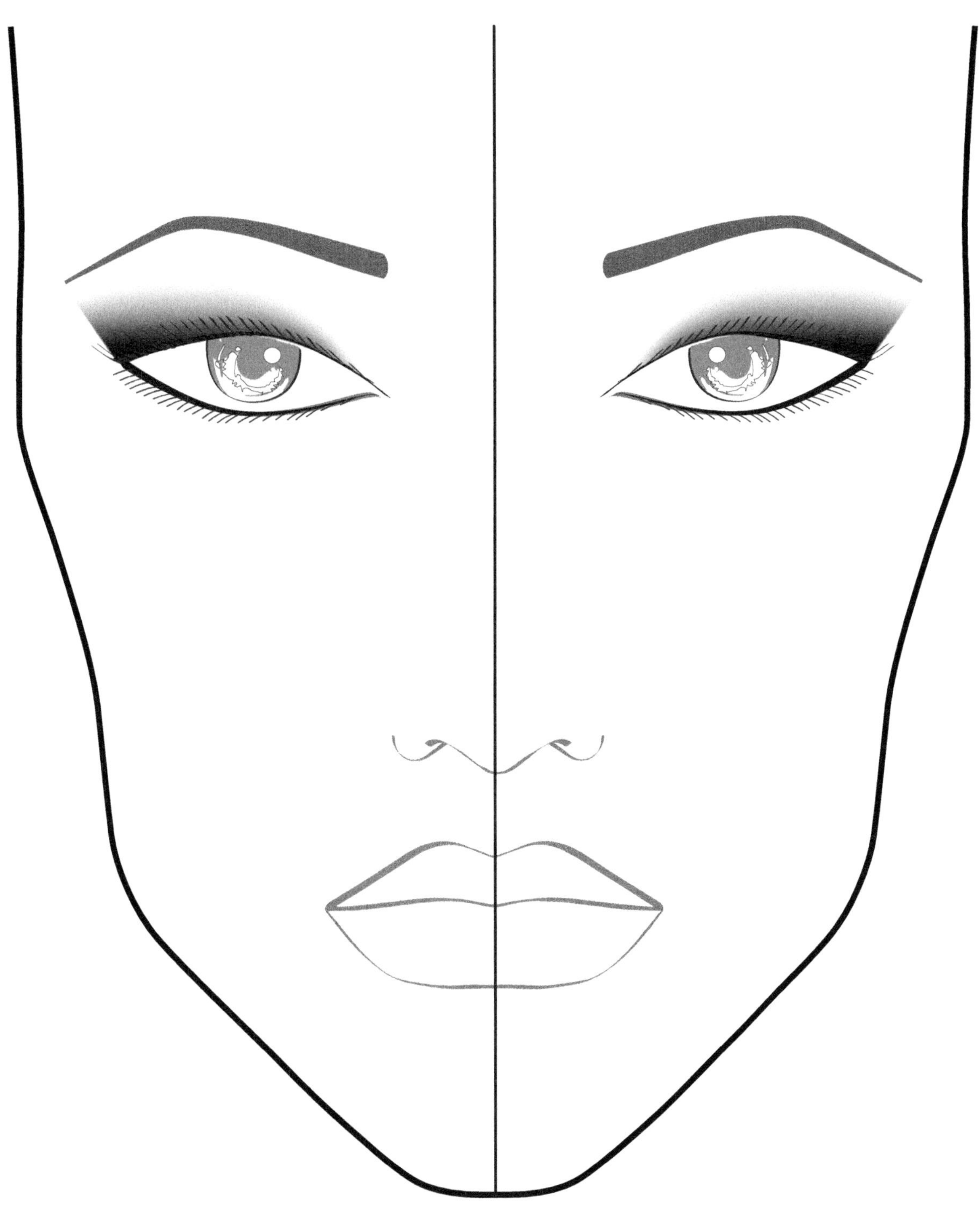

Always work from this imaginary middle line outwards

Always do one section of the face on one side, and then repeat the exact same application on the other.

It is liberating to achieve a great finish with so little makeup.

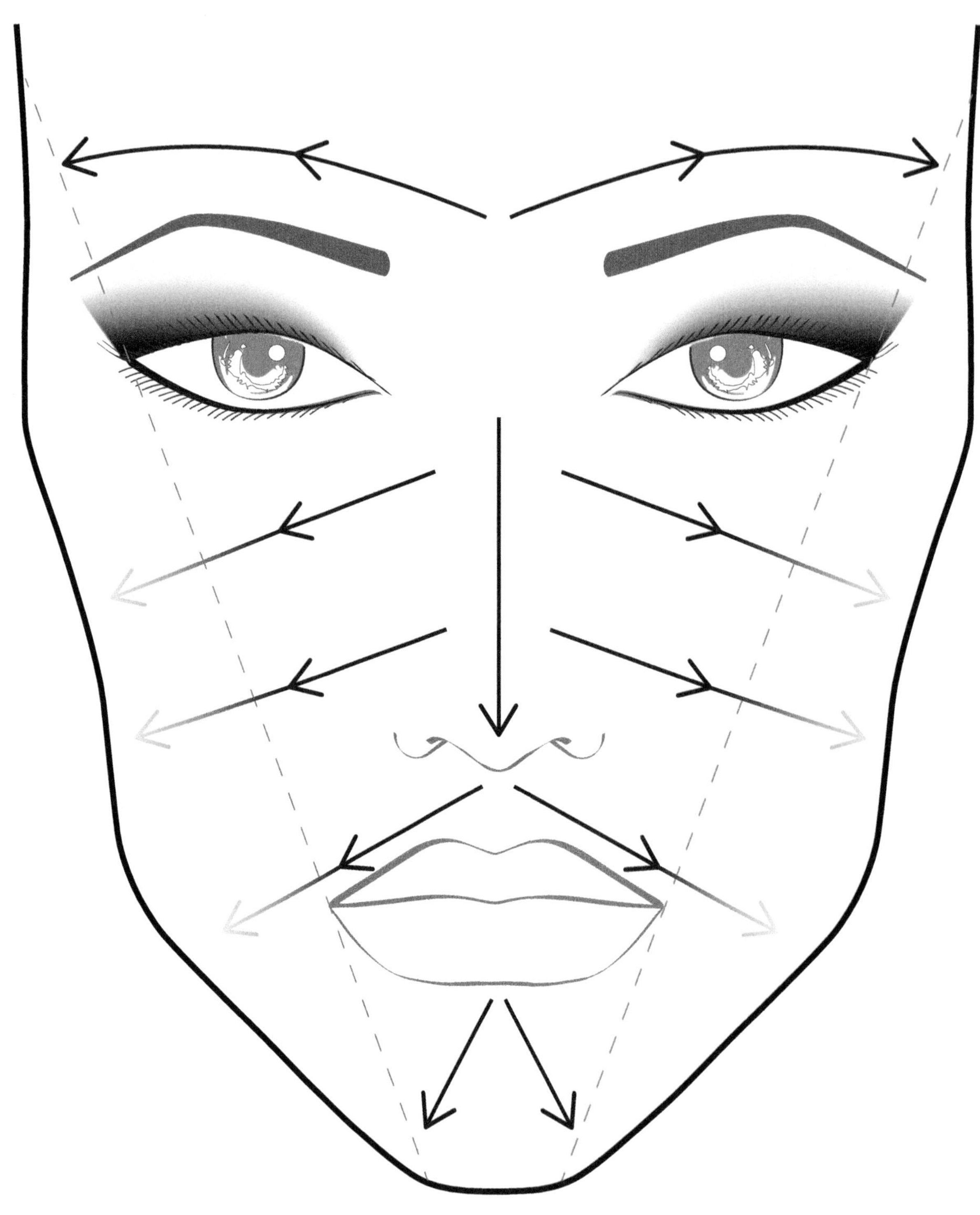

Step 2-
Skin Correction

Why:

This section is the heart of the *Face with a Heart* technique

The mantra of *Face with a Heart* makeup is to reduce (neutralize) the distractions and enhance the attractions.

This is most poignant when it comes to the appearance of skin. By neutralizing distractions, the main attractions come into clearer focus.

One of the biggest mistakes when working on the appearance of the skin is to focus too much on covering up what we don't want to see.

This can result in these effects:

- A mass amount of concealer placed directly on top of an area of concern, drawing the viewer's attention to that spot even more.
- A full coverage foundation applied to the same thickness over the whole face ending sharply along or just below the jaw line.
- Entire face blotted with matte powder to control the appearance of shine creating a dry mask look.

All of the above techniques are designed to solve a distraction problem, but in essence, they create more of a problem by drawing attention to the problem.

Face with a Heart approach to this dilemma is more sensitive to the outcome of the total look.

By neutralizing rather than covering distractions, less foundation is needed to create a flawless face without seeing the appearance of makeup.

The beauty of using corrector rather than concealer is that it completely serves the Face with a Heart method of makeup. It brightens the skin and Imperceptibly defines the sculpture of the face

Concealer definitely has its place in the appearance of skin. Besides confidently covering impossible to hide raised blemishes and significant dark spots, it may be used to diminish the appearance of unwelcome shadows and puffiness.

To be clear- no makeup looks like it does in manufactured digital and print media. What this technique does is gets the makeup closest to authentic perfection in real time.

Now is the time to reveal how the magic trick is done.

How:

The use of correctors/neutralizers on the skin will accomplish a few things at once. It will reduce the distractions without covering them up. This adds to a more skin-like, less makeup-y finish. It will also sculpt the heart of the face to maximize the face shape and the presence of the eye and lips within the heart line and the shape of cheeks outside the heart line.

One of the biggest concerns in makeup is the under eye area. Darkness distracts from the eyes and generally promotes a fatigued look.

Beyond neutralizing the darkness, this method redirects the way light plays under the eyes to create an upward/outward lift that highlights the heart and vault of the face.

To do this, work with a more geometric shaped application. Instead of following the round orbital eye socket with our product, reshape the under eye area to create the vaulted lifted appearance to the eye.

Each color serves a different purpose and its placement needs to be precise.

CORRECTOR COLORS DEFINED		SKIN TONE	CORRECTORS
Pink	Neutralizes and corrects darkness and brightens for light to medium skin tones	Light	
Green	Neutralizes and corrects redness for light to medium skin tones	Medium Light	
Light Yellow	Neutralizes and corrects redness and darkness for medium to medium-dark skin tones.	Medium	
Dark Yellow	Neutralizes and corrects redness and darkness for medium-dark to dark skin tones.(interchangeable with orange, depending on skin's undertone)	Medium Dark	
Orange	Neutralizes and corrects redness and darkness for medium-dark to dark skin tones. (interchangeable with deep yellow, depending on skin's undertone)	Dark	

Here's how it works.
Think of drawing a checkmark with the corrector/ concealer brush.

- Start at the inner corner of the eye, apply straight down along the side of the nose until pass the orbital eye socket bone (but above the nasal fold)
- Then in a straight, slightly upward angled direction, draw outwards past the outer corner of the eye and along the shelf of the cheekbone, allowing the product to trail off once past the outer corner of the eye.
- Now fill in the checkmark up to the bottom lashes/ eye liner with the corrector. It is important to get this corrector snug to the bottom eyelashes so no darkness remains.
- As with all makeup application, start with a small amount and build up to the desired coverage.
- The area of distraction will slowly fade into a neutral tone.
- Keep adding until no more is needed. That is just before the point when the area stars to look like the color of the corrector and not neutral anymore.
- The best way to blend without removing the product is to tap/press repeatedly with the pad of the middle finger (because it is the widest finger) until the product lays snugly in the skin and not on top.

If there are other areas of the face within the heart with distracting darkness, neutralize it by either stippling the corrector with your concealer brush or by putting the product on the pad of the middle finger and repeatedly tap/press until the darkness fades.

Remember that foundation follows next so no need to get full coverage now. Use just enough to neutralize the area.

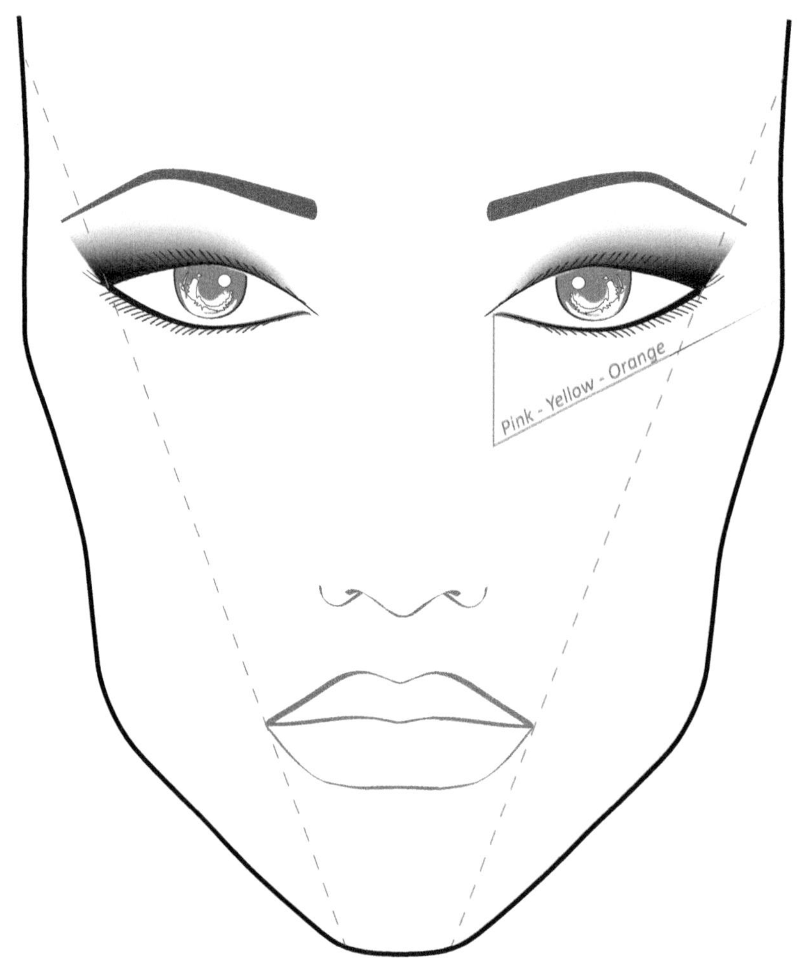

Next up: redness correctors

Green and yellow/orange are the redness correctors/neutralizers.

Green works with light to medium skin tones and yellow/orange work with medium-dark to dark skin tones.

Be specific with this application.

For the sake of this style of beauty makeup, the primary concern with pattern redness is within the interior of the heart of the face. Pattern redness is an area of skin that appears red rather than a red dot like a blemish. Focus on the redness up to the border line of the heart of the face. What this does is enhances the heart/vault of the face by isolating the clarity of skin-tone within the heart.

A note: Correctors are powerful makeup tools. Beyond neutralizing, they also brighten and heighten the skin where it is used. That is why it is most effective to use these products within the heart of the face only to achieve the lifted vaulted effect. By bordering the heart line, the face will lift beautifully. If used outside the heart line, they can diminish the effect of the *Face with a Heart.*

Facial contour and blush will be added outside the heart line so it is not as important to neutralize the redness outside the heart of the face.

Using a corrector/concealer brush, slowly brush on the green corrector over the redness until the redness is neutralized, visualizing the imaginary line from the outer corner of the lip to the outer corner of the eye.
If the color of the corrector begins to emerge, too much has been used. Stop there and stipple the corrector with a finger or foundation sponge. Avoid rubbing or wiping the corrector as that will reduce both efficacy of the corrector and face shape.

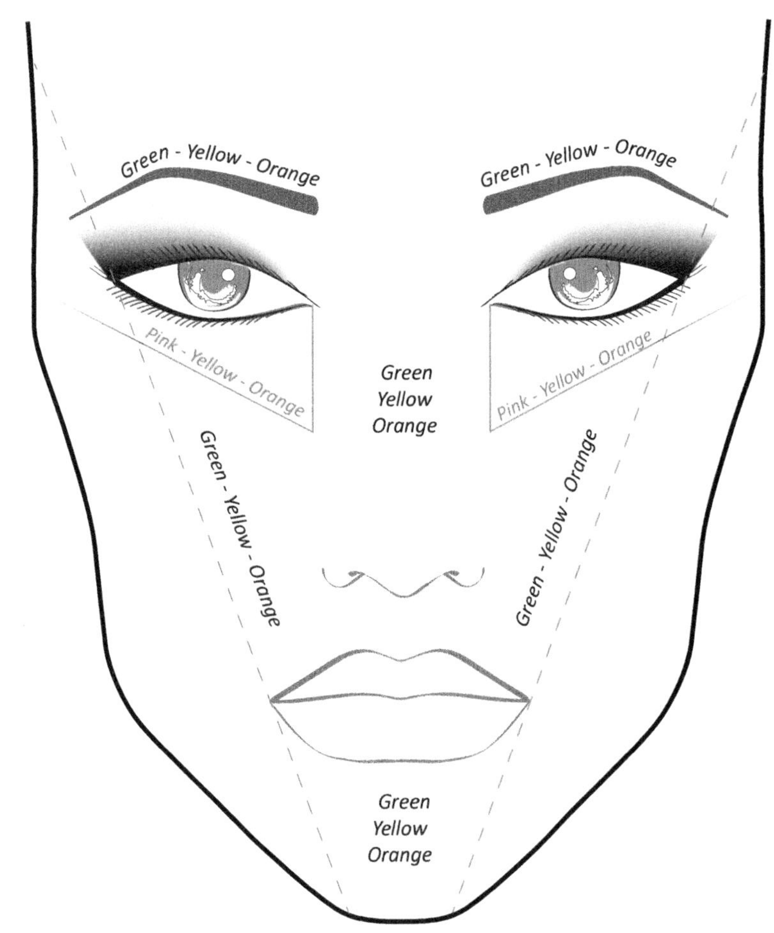

For some, the appearance of a shadow (not to be confused with darkness) created by a fold in the skin may also be neutralized by the use of a skin tone concealer.
There are two key areas where shadows may fall in the heart of the face. They are:

- The nasal labial fold which is that arched curve that travels from the nose flare as far down as to the outer edge of the lips.
- A frown line fold which is that arched curve that travels from the edge of the lips downward and creates the appearance of a frown.

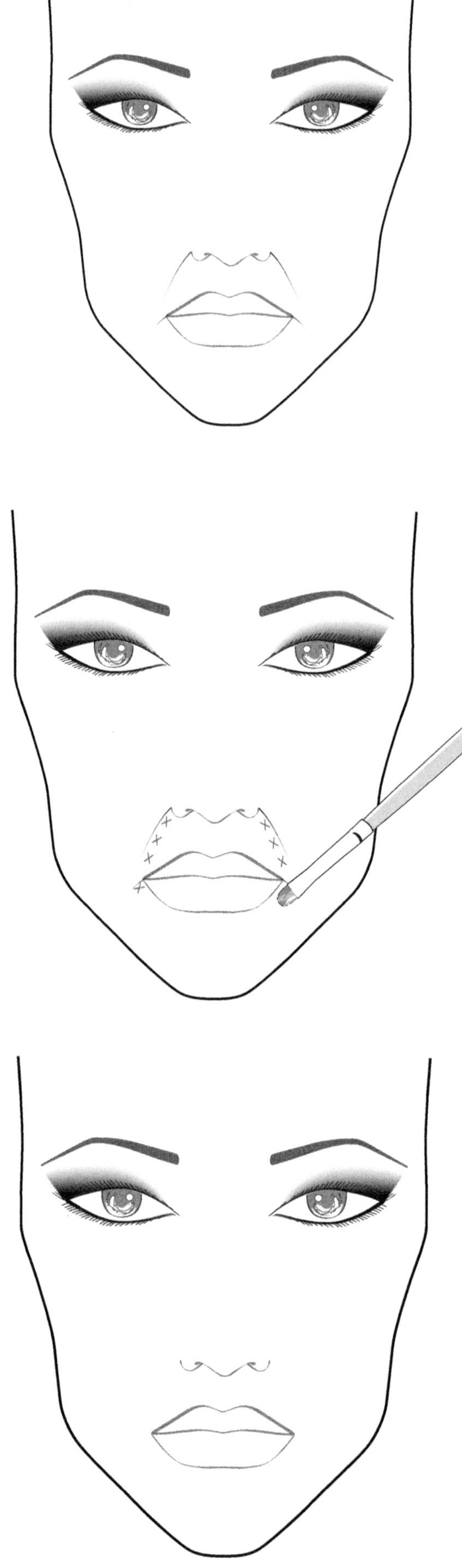

When correcting actual shadows, a slightly lighter than skin tone concealer works best to minimize the shadow when it appears in downward lighting situations.

Shadow Concealer

- Using the corrector/concealer brush, gently press the concealer under the fold of the skin where the shadow falls.

- Tap the concealer gently with fingertip to smooth and flatten it into the shadow and the skin.

- Gently setting all of the applied corrector with a small amount of translucent powder will prevent the foundation from thinning the corrector when the foundation is applied.

In essence, the objective is to lighten where the shadow falls to minimize its effect.

Only use this method on those who need it and, like all the other applications, don't overdo it.

The one other dominant corrector is mauve. Mauve is used more rarely and neutralizes a sallow skin tone. Once again, apply this only within the heart of the face.

Remember, the purpose of corrector is to reduce any discoloration distractions in order to optimally enhance the attractions of the eyes and lips within the heart line, and the contrast of facial contour and blush outside the heart line.

Step 3 – Foundation

Why:

To maximize the clarity and evenness of color of the skin.

The eyes and lips are the focal point features of every beauty makeup, and the only way to truly achieve this is to make the skin appear as naturally flawless as possible. The desired effect is noticing the skin first because there is something sensually compelling about a smooth, flawless skin. This is a great achievement for any makeup application because beautiful looking skin indicates a healthy, young acting skin which radiates beauty and light.

When skin is flawless, the main attractions (eyes and lips) pop into even more clear focus because they are competing with nothing else on the face for attention.
For beauty makeup, the foundation on the skin must not attract more attention than the eyes and lips. It will become a distraction and the concept of beauty is lost by over-using the foundation. It is a fine balanced line between a flawless finish and a foundation finish. It is here that the makeup artist must use the most discerning eye and technique to get just the right application for a flawless finish.

How:

- Put small amount of foundation in the hand not holding the brush.
- Using the tip of the foundation brush only, place a small amount of foundation on brush.
- Starting from the center of the face, brush outwards at a very slight downward angle.
- Continue to stroke from the center of the face outward until all of the foundation has blended into the skin.
- For a more 'skin-like' finish, try not to go for full coverage with the first layer.
- Apply foundation to the face in sections, giving the first layer a chance to set before applying a second layer (if needed).
- After applying first layer of foundation, stand 3 feet back from the mirror and assess where more coverage is desired. The heart of the face should be free and clear of any distractions.

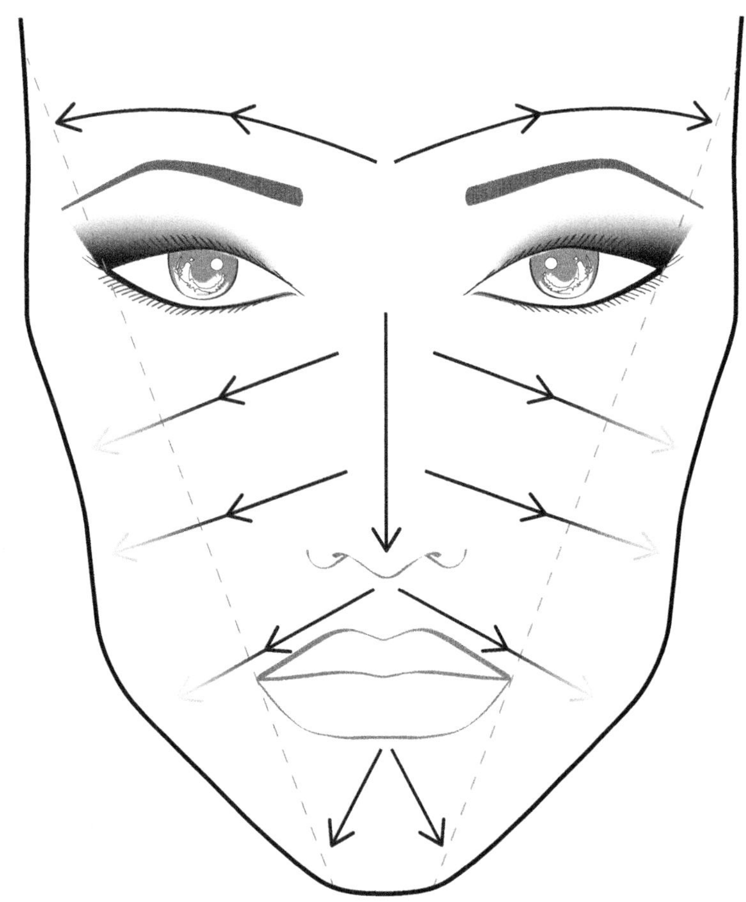

Here is a suggested order of application.

Split the face right down the middle form forehead to chin.

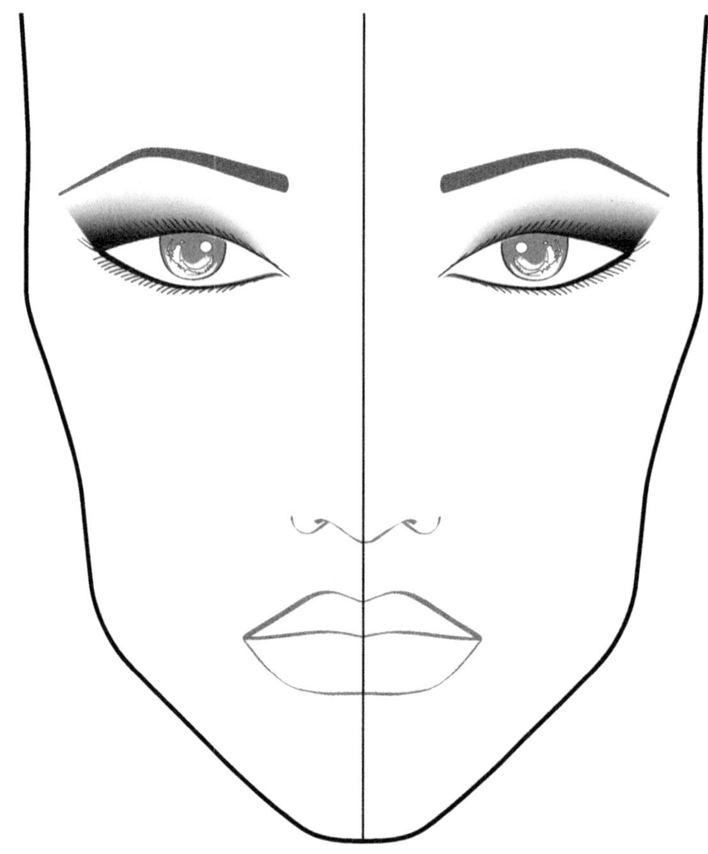

Always work from this imaginary middle line outwards. Think of foundation as a top coat, the same way top coat is used on nails. Top coat is clear and brings out the luster of the nail. Foundation, when applied like a top coat, brings out the luster of the skin instead of covering the luster. The suggested ratio of corrector to foundation is 80% corrector to 20% foundation. Adjust this ratio to the needs of the skin.

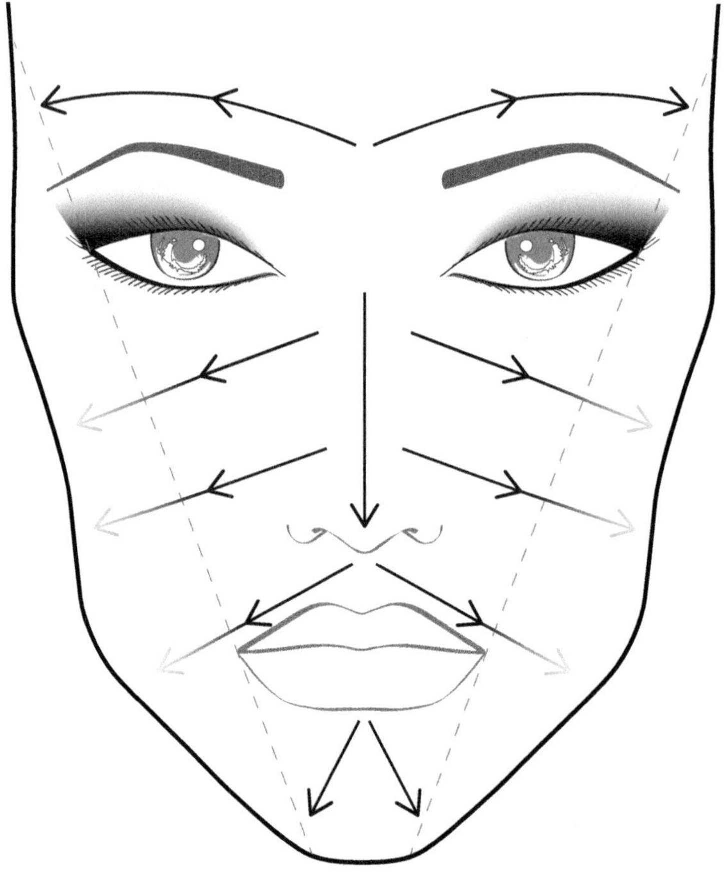

Always do one section of the face on one side, and then repeat the exact same application on the other.

For example:

- Starting at the side of nose, apply foundation to one cheek, then to the other.
- Starting from between eyebrows, fan across the forehead on one side, then the other.
- Under the nose, brush outwards, then repeat on other side
- From the center of the chin outwards and slightly downwards and repeat on other side.
- Stripe down center of nose and blend down the sides of the nose on both sides.

Things to remember for the best foundation application

- Within the 'heart of the face' is where the finish is most flawless.
- Once outside the heart line, the foundation can diminish from a level 10 to a level 1 as it moves towards the jawline and hairline.
- Always completely blend out what is on the skin before applying more foundation to the skin. Create a thin veil of coverage that can be built on when and where it is needed.
- Do not apply an additional layer of foundation over a layer you just applied. This gives time for the existing layer to set (dry).
- Allow the brush to flick off the jawline rather than run the brush along the edge of the jaw line. This will create a disappearing finish as opposed to a border finish along the jaw line.
- Finally, use the corrector brush to apply the foundation very thinly under the eye area in the same shape as the corrector. In most scenarios, this provides all the coverage necessary under the eye area.

The best advice to applying foundation is: "where you need it-when you need it."

Step 4 - Powder

Why:

Powder is used after foundation to set (dry) the makeup.

Powder is designed to initially dry the wet part of the foundation so that it sets as quickly as possible to the skin to achieve the longest lasting finish. Without powder, the moisture content of the foundation will continue to move as it is warmed by the body's natural temperature. Most foundation will maintain for 4 hours without powder and 8 hours with powder.

How:

- Fill up the sides of the powder brush with translucent powder.
- Press/pat the powder on to the wet foundation with the side of the powder brush all over the face
- Allow the powder to set/dry the foundation completely.
- Brush the excess powder off from the center of the face outwards leaving smooth, clean brush strokes to direct the traffic of light on the skin so that it will heighten skin brightness and luminosity.

As a final powder step, put a little skin tone translucent powder on the edge of a wedge sponge and press the sponge right up to the bottom eye line and the under eye area. This will flatten and set the foundation closest to the eyes, and will prevent makeup from running under the eyes.

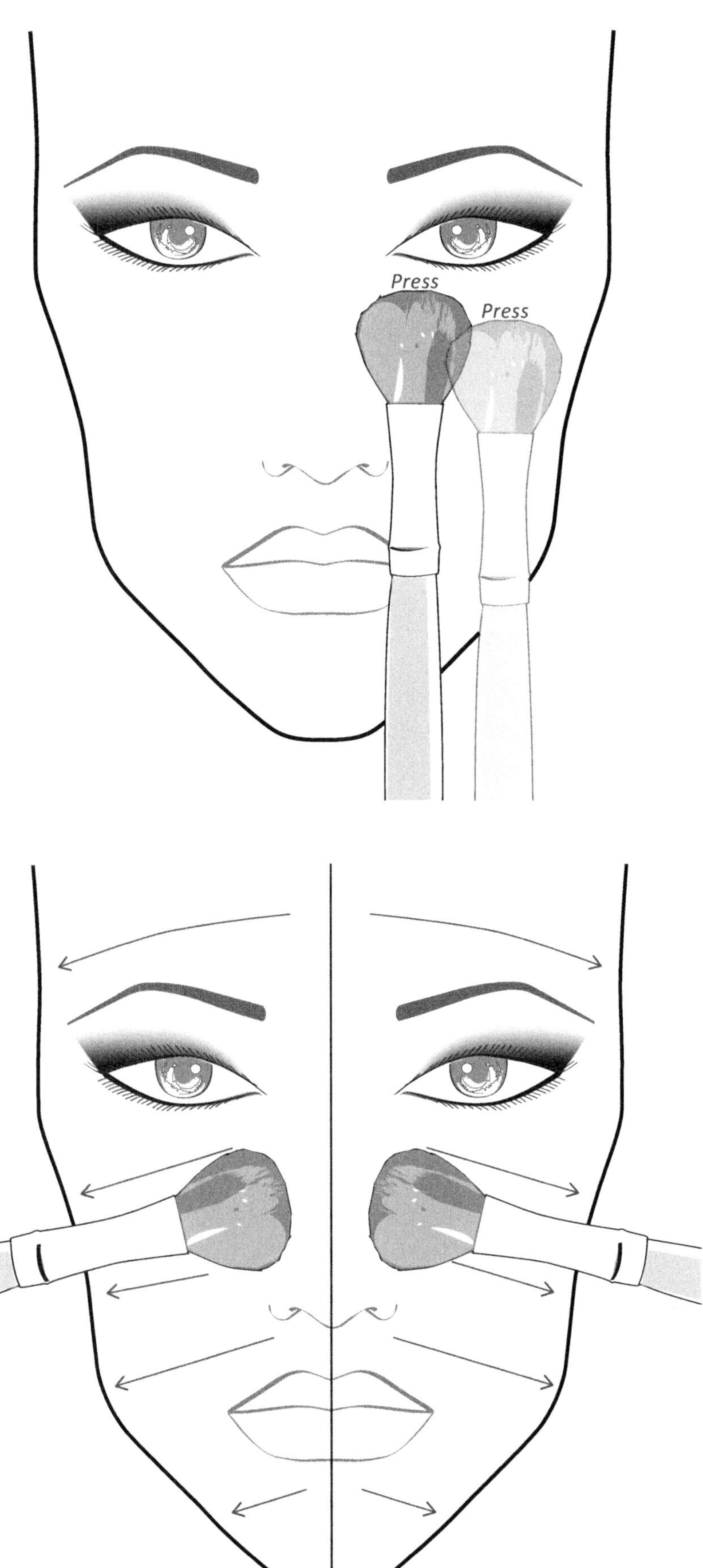

Lips

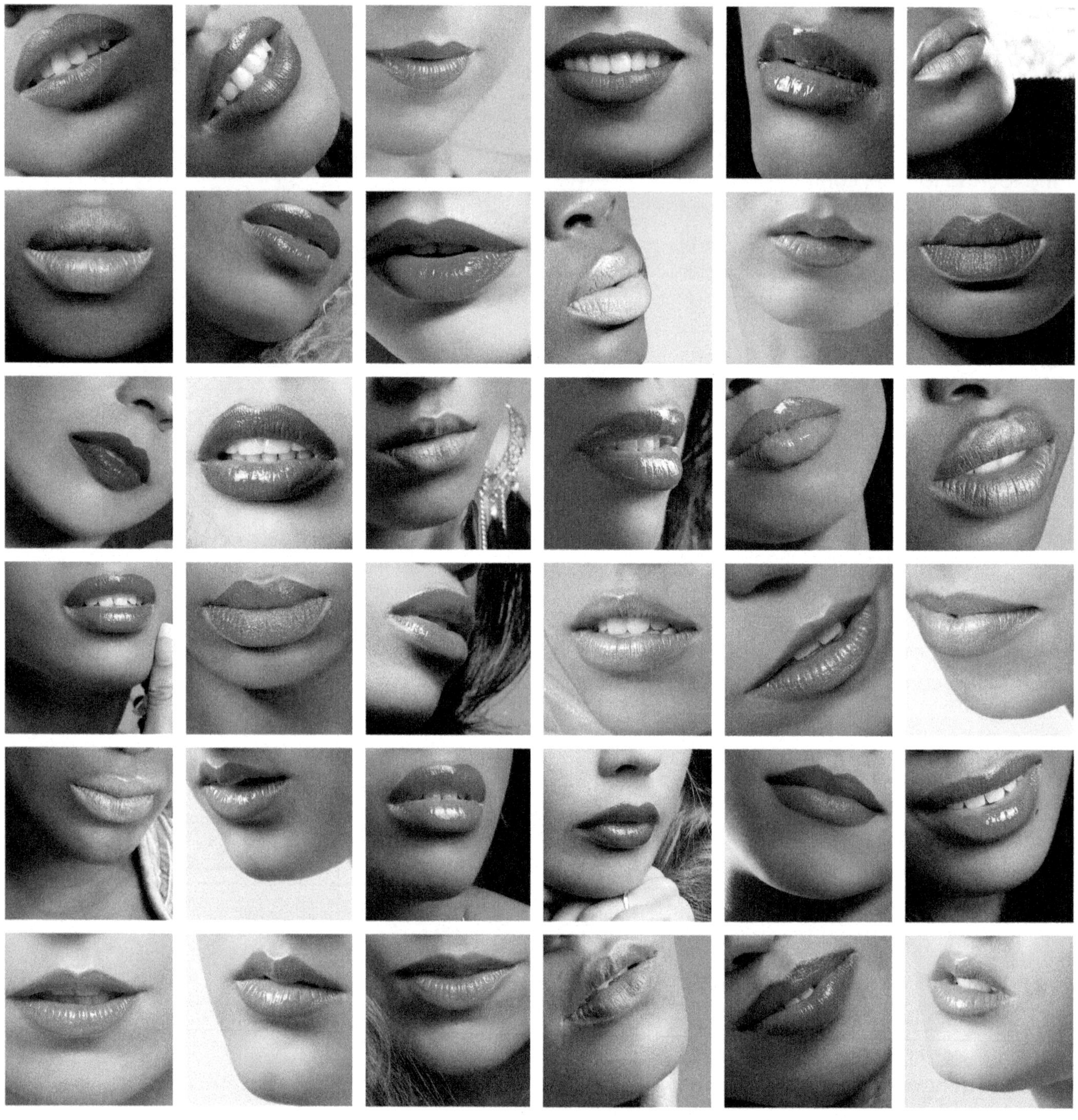

Why:

To highlight the second most important feature of the face.

In the *Face with a Heart* world of beauty, the lips compose the bottom half of the heart and are, by themselves, a heart within a heart. Our two main communicators are our eyes and lips. It is therefore vital to isolate the lips so they are able to most effectively serve as the powerful communicators that they are.

Lips are also sensuous and sexy. We eat, kiss, and do many other things with our lips. Lips play a very important part in the world of beauty makeup and need to be treated as thus.

The lips also serve as the base of the heart of the face. To heighten the vault/lift of the face, make lips tall, not wide.

Tall lips accomplish a couple of important beauty elements.

- Tall lips maximize the center of the mouth by becoming the fullest part of the lip.
- Tall lips help narrow the base of the heart to create a more lifted vaulting energy to the face.

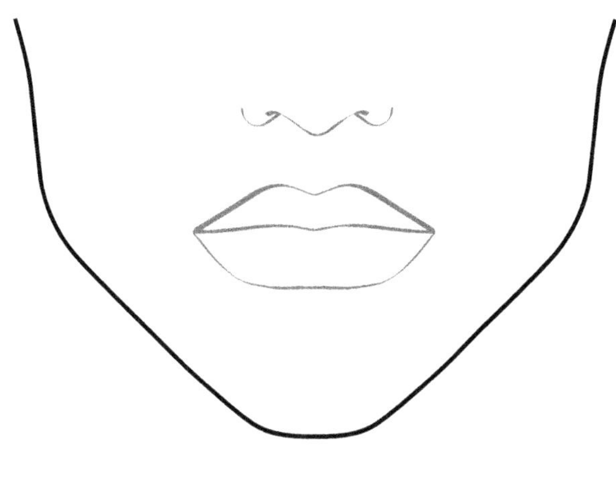

Step 1- Lip liner

In order to make lips appear tall, we round out the center of the lips and undercut the outer corner of the lips.The illusion is a taller lip. Here is how to do it.

How:

Lip liner is used to define the shape of the lips.
It can simultaneously re-define the shape of the lips plus provide asymmetrical correction.

Bottom Lip Line

The concept is to make the bottom lip appear as a glass of water that is being tipped so that the water has come right up to the edge of the glass. It appears at any moment the water will spill out of the glass but it doesn't.

- Begin by using a lip pencil to enhance the center of the mouth.
- Trace along the natural lip line at the center of the bottom lip.
- Then allow the lip liner to drop just below the center of the lip line to create the appearance of fullness to the center of the bottom lip.
- Where the bottom lip begins to curve upwards towards the outer corner of the mouth, sketch a strong straight line to the inside corner of the outer corners of the lips.
- Fill the interior of the liner into the lip a little to really connect the new shape liner to the lip.
- This illusion will push the center of the mouth more forward and keep lips from looking too wide.

Top Lip Line

The concept here is to create a slightly swollen appearance to the upper lip from just outside the center 'V' to halfway down the upper lip. This will create height and fullness to the upper lip.

- Start by sketching in the 'V' shape at the center of the upper lip. Strive for symmetry.
- Next sketch the top lip line from the peak of the 'V' of the upper lip to the inside corner of the outer corners of the mouth.
- Then, if more fullness is desired, slightly round above the lip line from the peak of the 'V' to halfway down the upper lip.
- It is vital that the lip line appear connected to the actual lip line so build up from the existing lip line to create this effect successfully.
- Fill the interior of the liner into the lip a little to really connect the new shape liner to the lip
- Finally, sketch with a lip brush along the lip liner to soften the interior edge and marry it to the lips.

Step 2 - Lip color

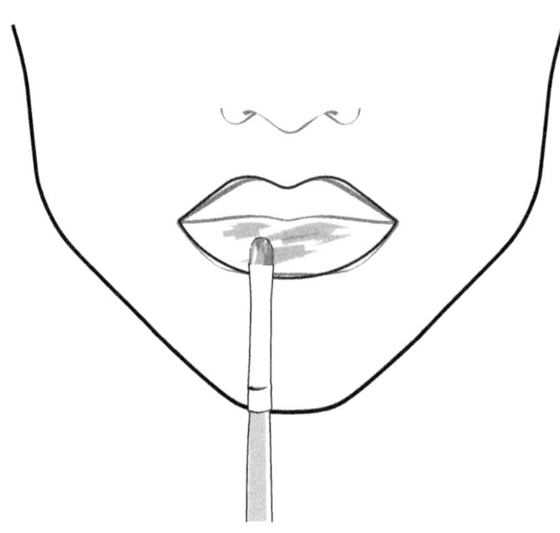

Regardless of the intensity of makeup being applied from natural to dramatic, the goal is to make the lips appear as if they are the color that they are wearing.

The alternative is that the lips appear as if they are coated in the color they are wearing. Try to avoid this look at all cost. It never applies to beauty makeup.

- The trick is to forcefully sketch a small amount of lip color into the lip with a lip brush until the pigment of the color gets under the skin of the lips.
- From here, more can be applied in the same fashion to increase the intensity of the color.
- When the desired intensity has been fulfilled, the lips appear to be that color, not 'wearing' that color.

- Finish the lips by using a small amount of foundation on a concealer brush and clean up with a razor sharp finish around the exterior of the lips right along the outside of the lip line.
- This technique allows to 'photo shop' the shape of the mouth and color application to perfection.

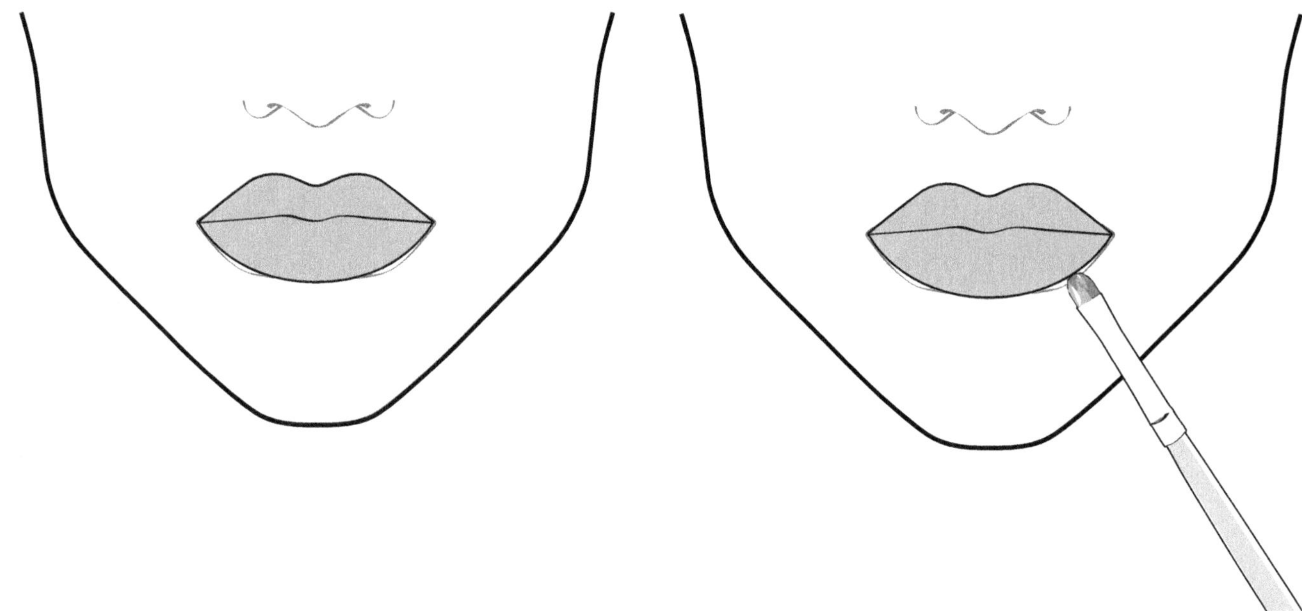

Step 3 - Gloss

- Gloss is an optional final top coat to the lips. To maximize light reflection on the lips, apply vertically with the grain of the lip's skin tissue. Light will bounce best off the lips when applied this way. Keep gloss slightly within the edge of the lip line to allow room for gloss spread, which inevitably happens when lips rub together.

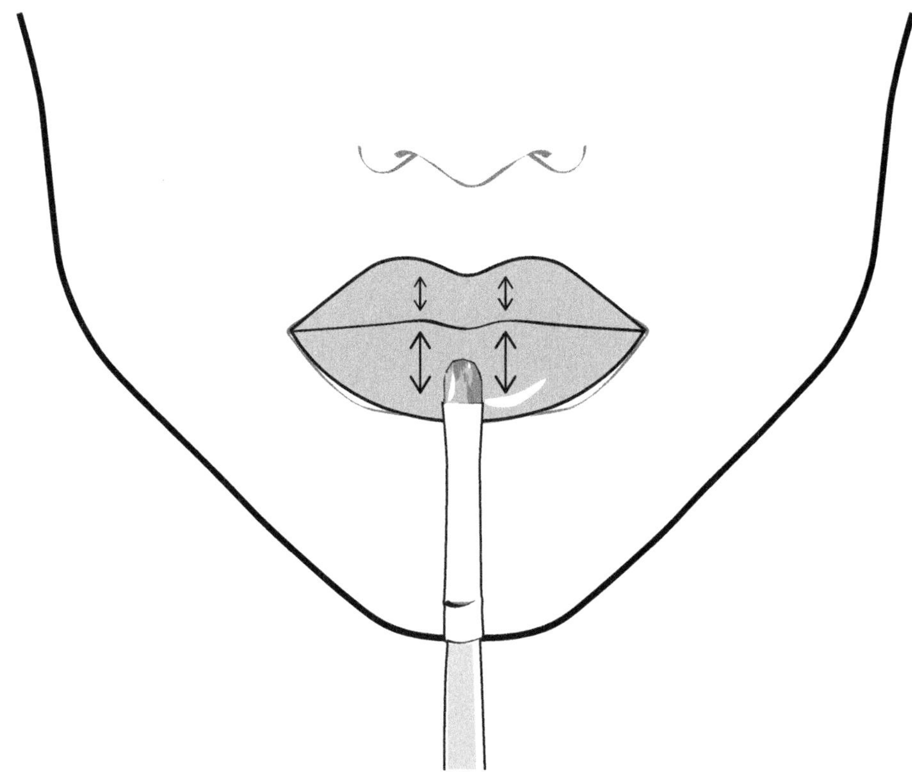

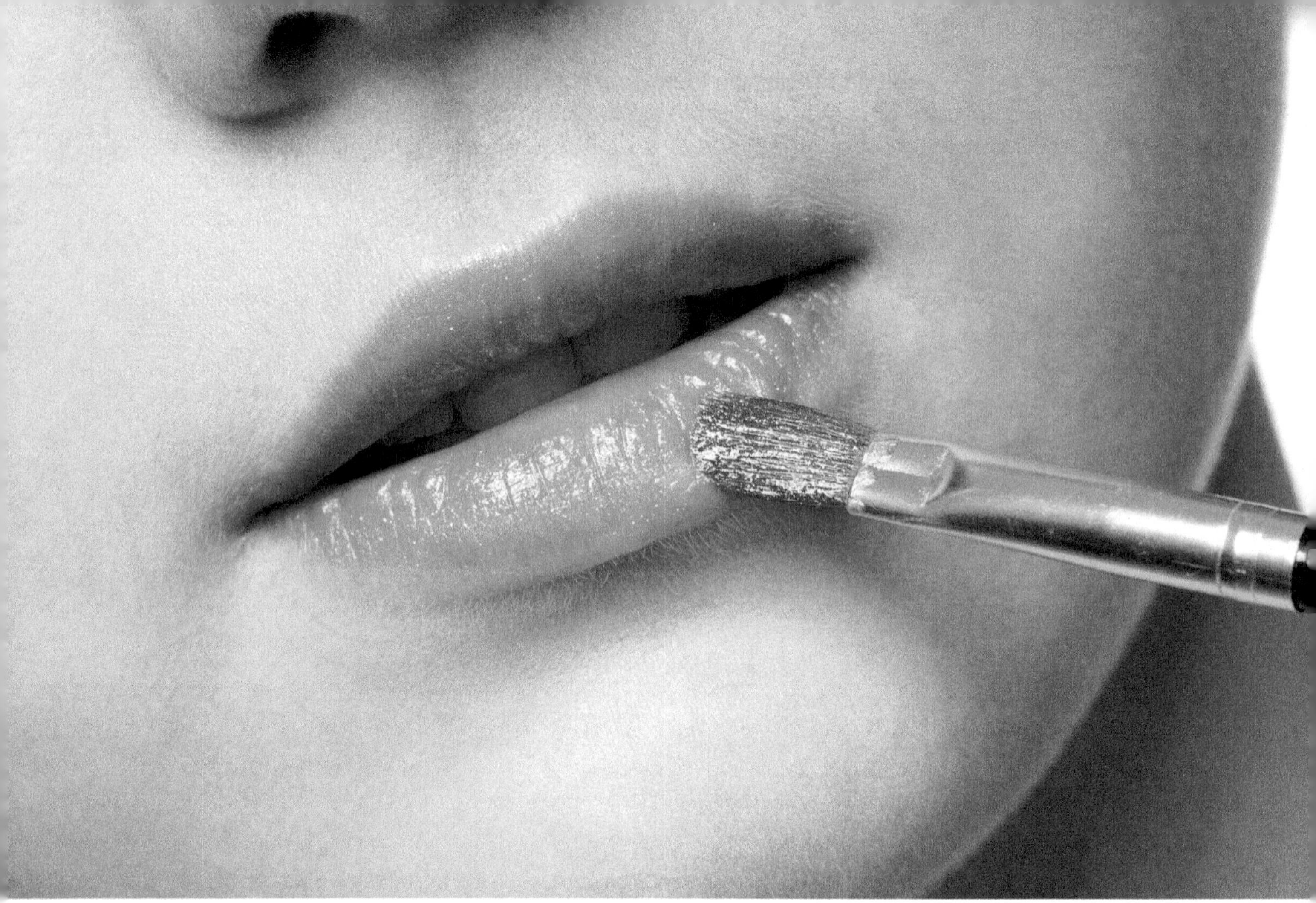

The eyes and lips are finished.

Now, work outside the heart of the face to better define and border the heart of the face.

Cheeks

Step 1- Cheek contour

Why:

Facial contouring further defines symmetry and highlights the heart of the face, and is used to create the illusion of a more defined cheekbone.
Facial contouring is also used to balance more specific parts of the face including the jawline, nose, and forehead, as well as helping to correct the overall appearance of the shape of the face. This type of contouring is known as corrective contouring.
One of the results of using correctors and foundation is that the skin's natural highlights (reflection) and lowlights (shadow) of color is neutralized everywhere on the face. This creates a flat, one-dimensional appearance to the face. Through the use of facial contouring, a more precise, balanced and multi-dimensional shape re-emerges on the skin. The face shape; however, will now be more beautifully enhanced because skin tone is not competing with distractions anymore.

Unlike the *Face with a Heart* approach up to now, where each technique works on every face, facial contouring may vary slightly or greatly from face to face.

This manual will address the generic contour of the cheek as it affects the Heart of the face only and not attempt to break-down unique approaches for every face shape.

How:

It is first necessary to breakdown the anatomy of the cheekbone to understand where and why contour is applied.
The cheek has three aspects in beauty makeup.

- Shelf- This is the top of the cheek bone where it first starts to round outward away from the center of the face and catches the most reflection of light.
- Crown- This is the outer edge of the cheek bone a quarter circle down from the shelf.
- Contour- This is where the cheek bone begins to roll back under from the crown. This is where contour is applied.
- Contour stops being applied at the base of the cheekbone as it rolls back down to meet the hollow of the cheek.
- Do not apply contour in the hollow of the cheek. This creates a sunken, unhealthy look. The purpose of contour is to lift the cheekbone and taper the face towards the heart of the face.

Contour shade needs to appear like a natural shadow. To get an idea of this shade, hold your hand along the cheek with the palm parallel to the floor.

Observe the color of the shadow created by your hand. Use a darker powder, blush, or matte bronzer that is close to the color of the natural shadow created by the shade of your hand.

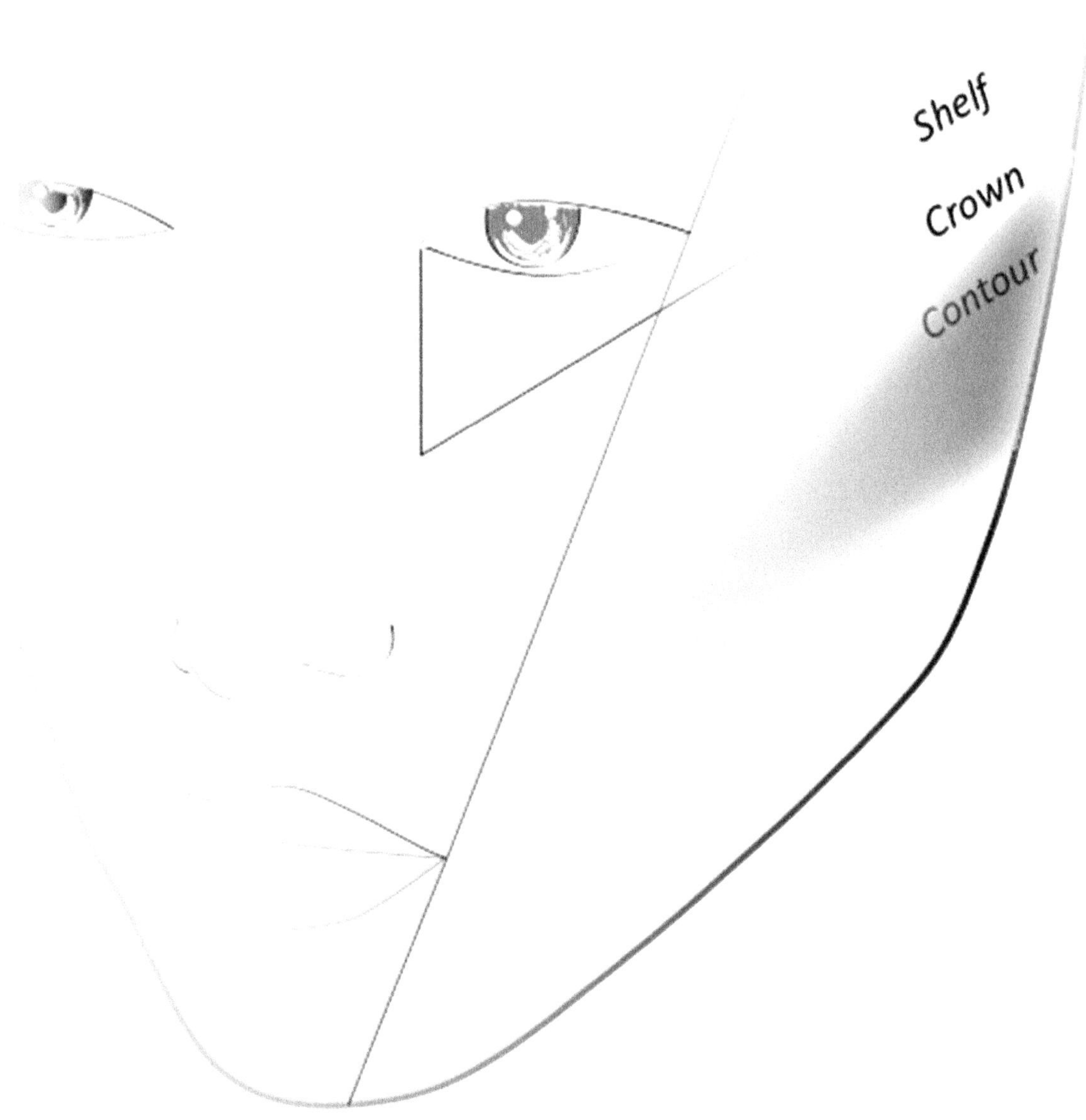

- Put a small amount of contour product on face contour brush.
- Start at the cheek and contour about one inch forward from the ear.
- Brush along the underside of cheekbone.
- For most anatomy, the brush goes towards the outer half of upper lip.
- Do not allow contour to pass the heart line.
- Apply methodically to both sides of the face to strike a balance. Go back and forth from side to side until balance is met.

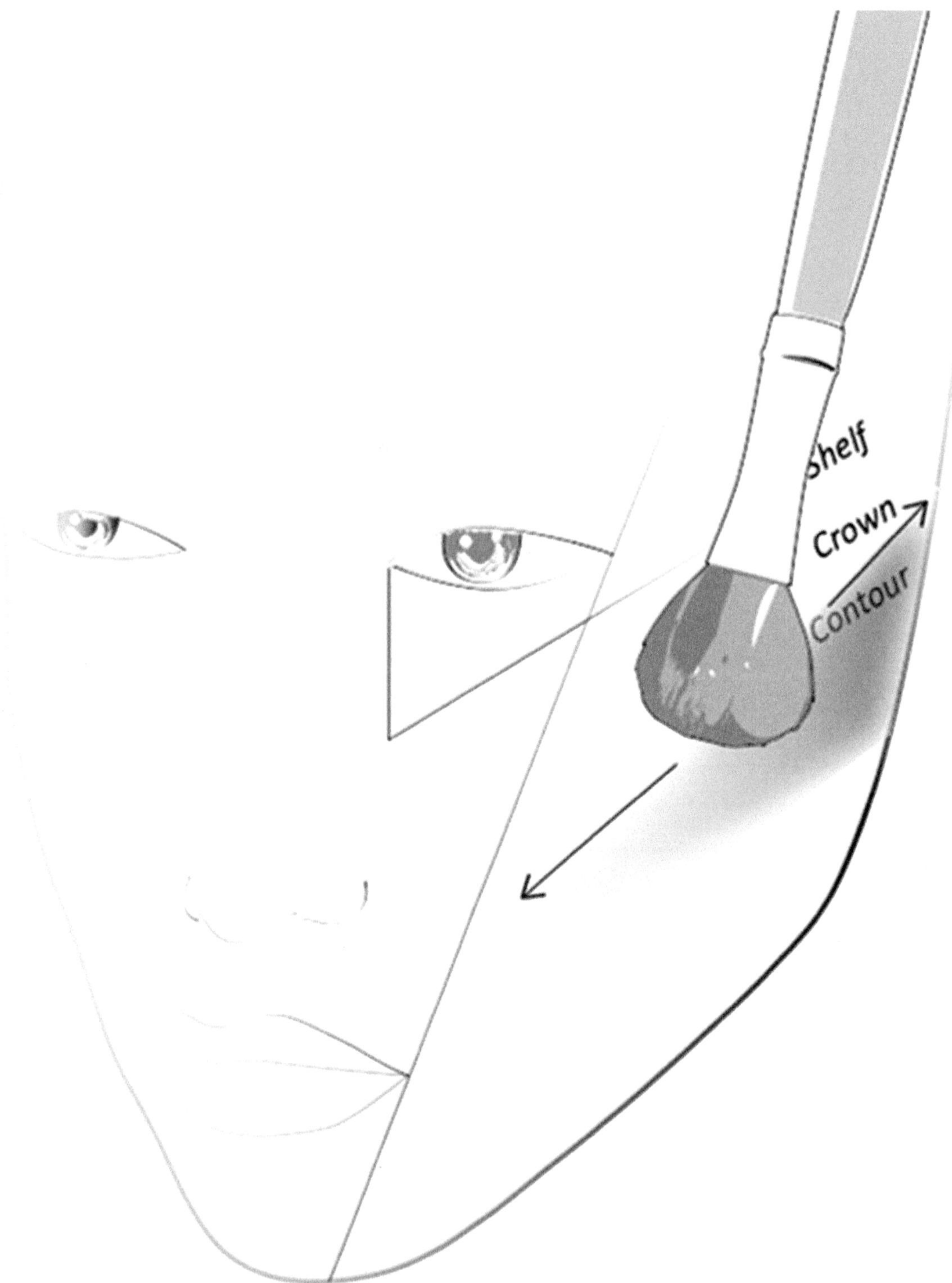

Step 2 -
Blend cheek contour

Often after applying the contour, there are visible edges along the upper and lower borders of the contour application.
It is necessary to buff out these edges to make the contour appear natural.

- Put translucent powder used to set the model's foundation on the tip of a clean blush brush.
- Squeeze the base of the blush brush hairs to make the brush firmer.
- In a back and forth motion, buff along the upper and lower edge of the contour application to soften the edge of the application.

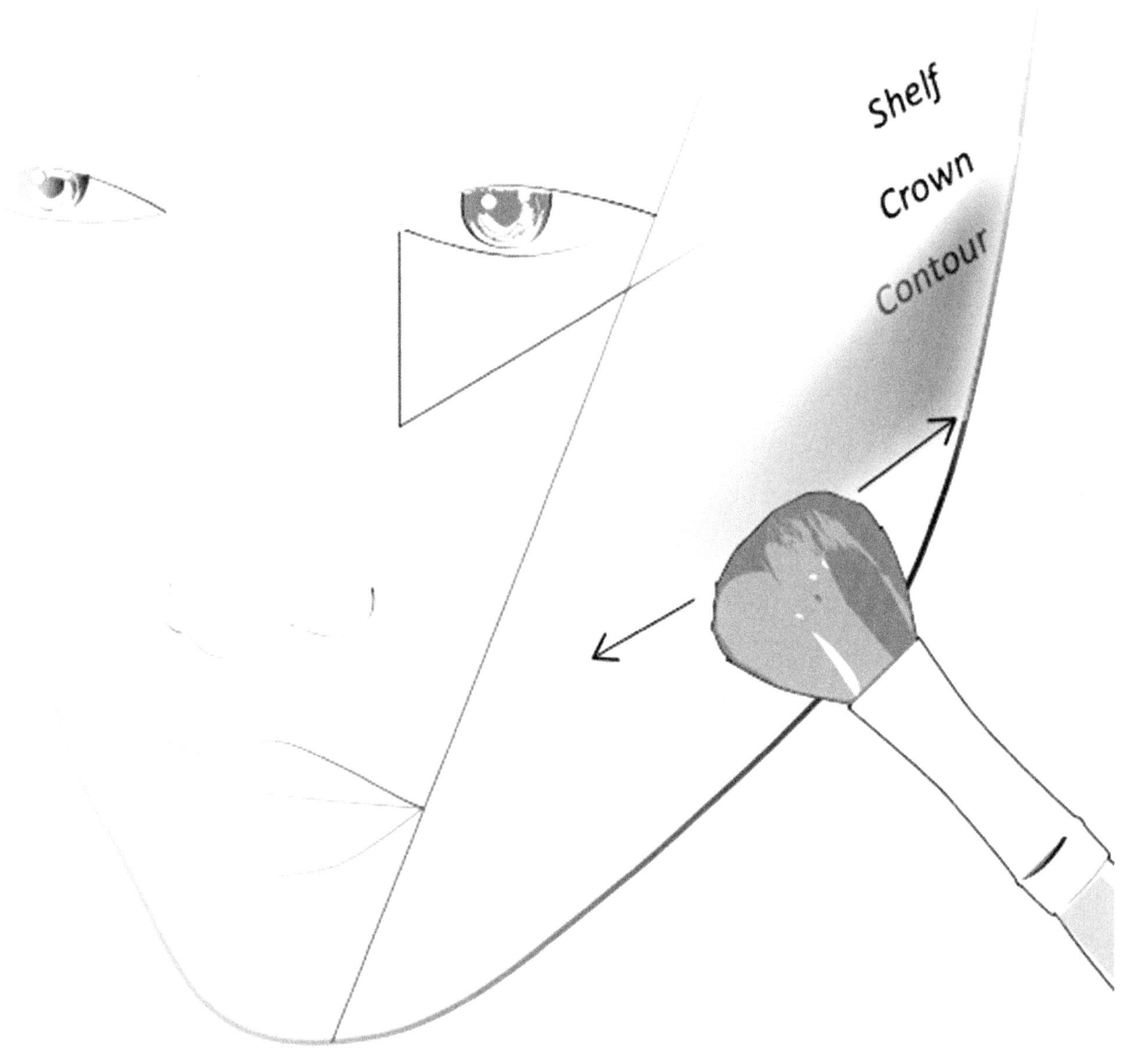

- Be careful not to buff over the whole contour as it will diminish the effect of the contour by lightening the whole contour.

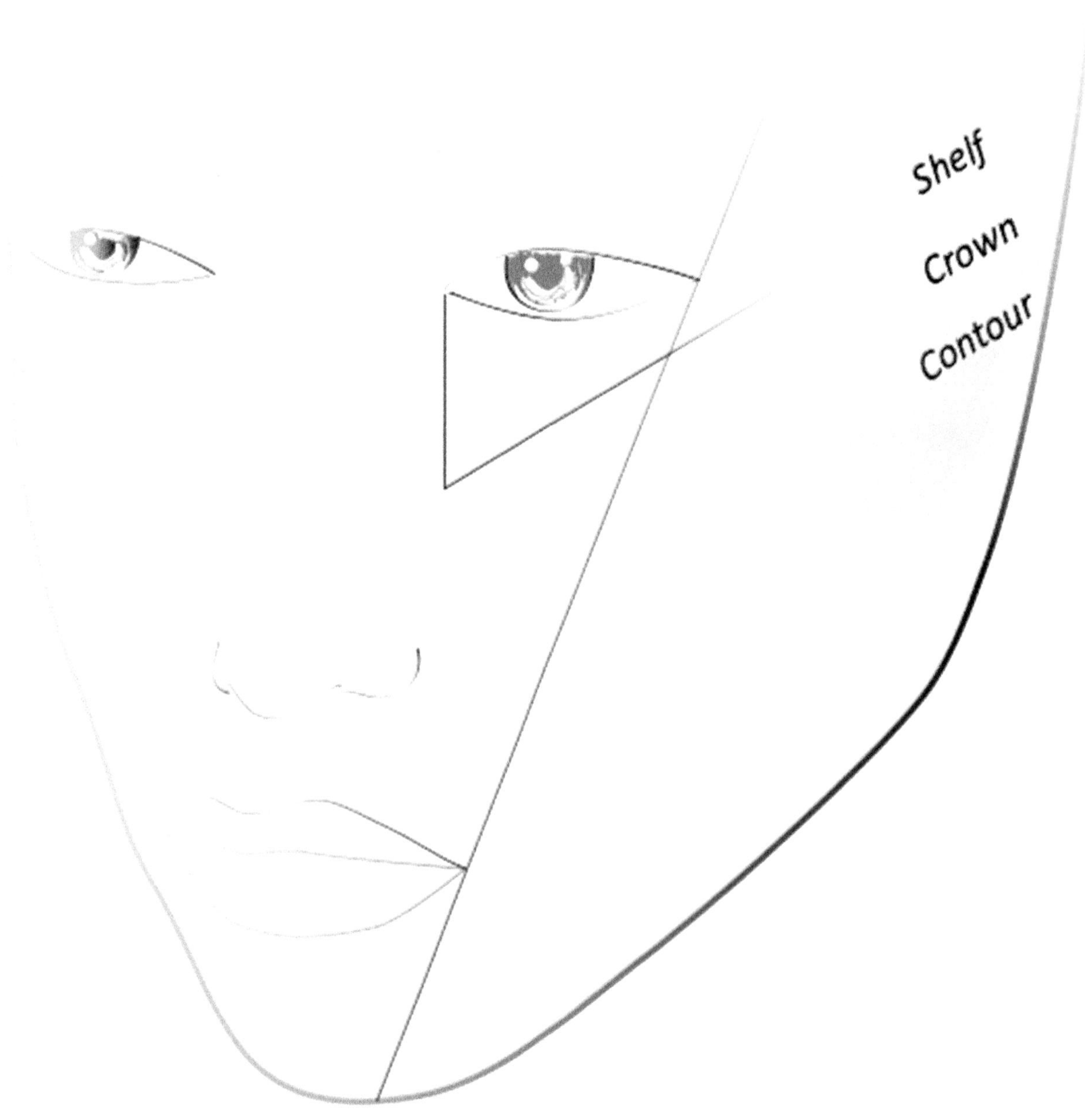
Shelf
Crown
Contour

Step 3 - Powder blush

Why:

To simulate and control the positioning of the cheeks natural production of color.

One of the results of using correctors and foundation is that the skin's natural production of color is neutralized everywhere on the face. This creates a flat, one-dimensional appearance to the face. Besides facial contouring, blush adds the next element of dimension to the face. It also greatly affects the appearance of the heart of the face by acting as a border just along the outside of the heart.

A fresh cheek color indicates a healthy skin and thus works well with the overall concept of authentic beauty makeup.

How:

This technique is designed to create the most natural looking appearance of color in the cheeks. Remember, the desire is not to wear color on cheeks, but cheeks to be that color.

This 3-2-1 technique will simulate the cheeks natural flushing as opposed to a topically applied look.

Powder blush: 3-2-1

- Pat the tip of the blush brush on to the blush color.
- Tap off the excess
- Smile or ask model to smile.
- The part of the cheek that rises up the most is where the first blush is applied. We call this the 'energy' of the cheek (this area is often called the apple of the cheek. As this placement is more precise, the energy of the cheek is preferred.) This means the place where the face moves the most in the cheek area.
- For placement, the first blush application goes along and outside the heart line in the energy of the cheek. This will further define and enhance the heart of the face.
- In a systematic fashion, pat the brush 3 times in the energy of the cheek.
- Now move up to the center of the cheekbone just along the top side of the contour application and pat 2 times.
- Next move back a little more towards the hairline and pat 1 time.
- Repeat this on the other side of the face.

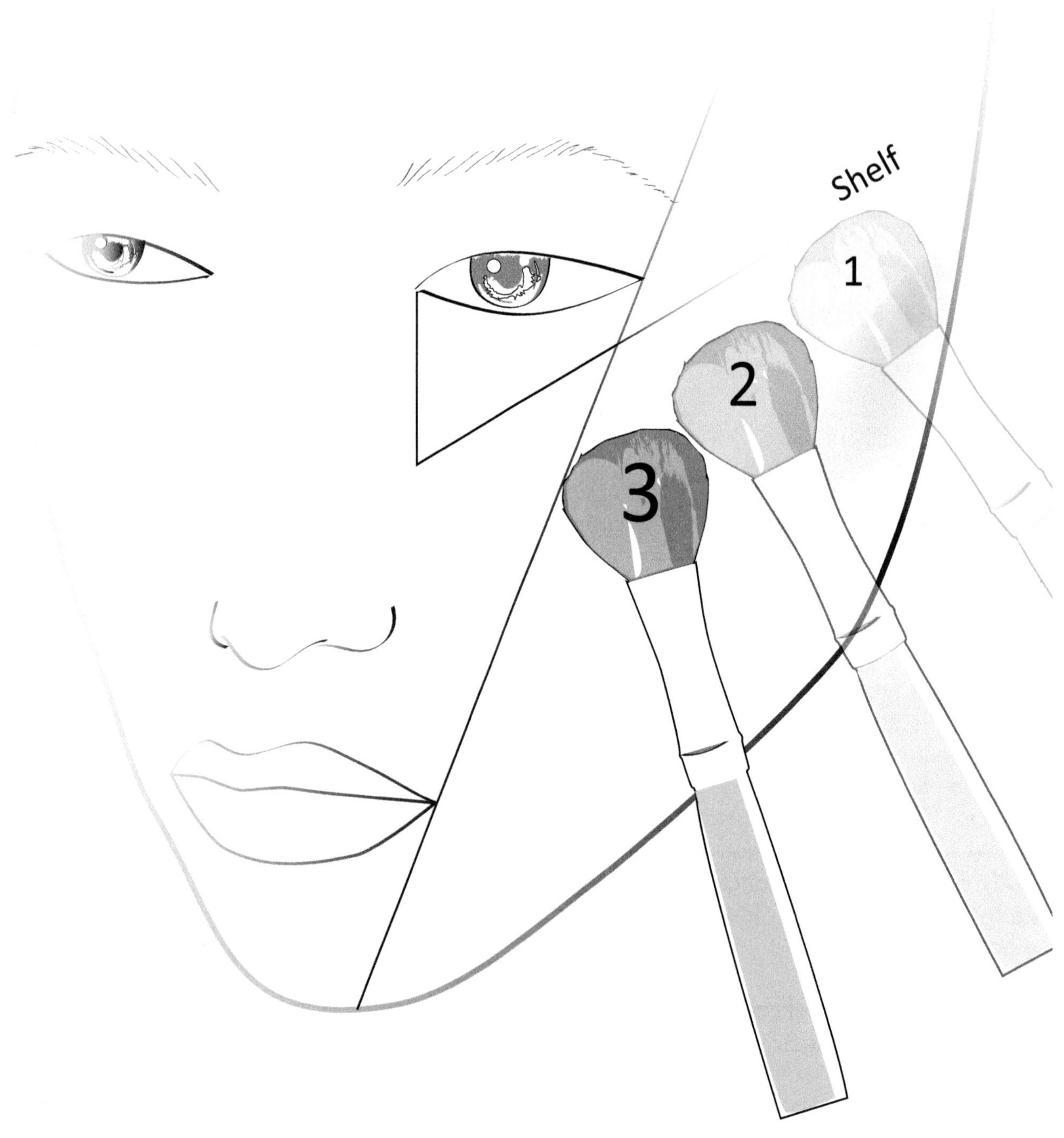

Go back and forth from cheek to cheek until the desired intensity and balance is met.
or

Step 4 - Cream blush

- Put cream blush on tip of middle finger
- Make 3 dots along the cheekbone in the exact same places described in the powder blush section and in the same order.

- By default, the first dot will have more color and the consequent dots will have less as the amount of cream blush lessens with each dot.
- Starting at the first dot closest to the heart line and with a clean finger, use the palm side of your finger and blend blush by working in a circular motion.
- Slowly work back to the hair line.
- This technique shall disperse the cream blush evenly and smoothly.

For skin that tends to absorb cheek color rapidly, it is suggested to layer the cream and powder blush. In this scenario, apply the cream blush first and the powder blush over the cream blush using the exact application techniques as described above.

Step 5 - Highlight cheek bone

An optional last step to both powder and cream blush is to highlight the shelf of the cheekbone.

The purpose of this is to further heighten the appearance of the cheekbone and add a glow just outside the eyes.

Highlighter comes in different forms; such as powder, cream, liquid.

They are all applied the same way; by using your finger or a brush to apply the highlighter.

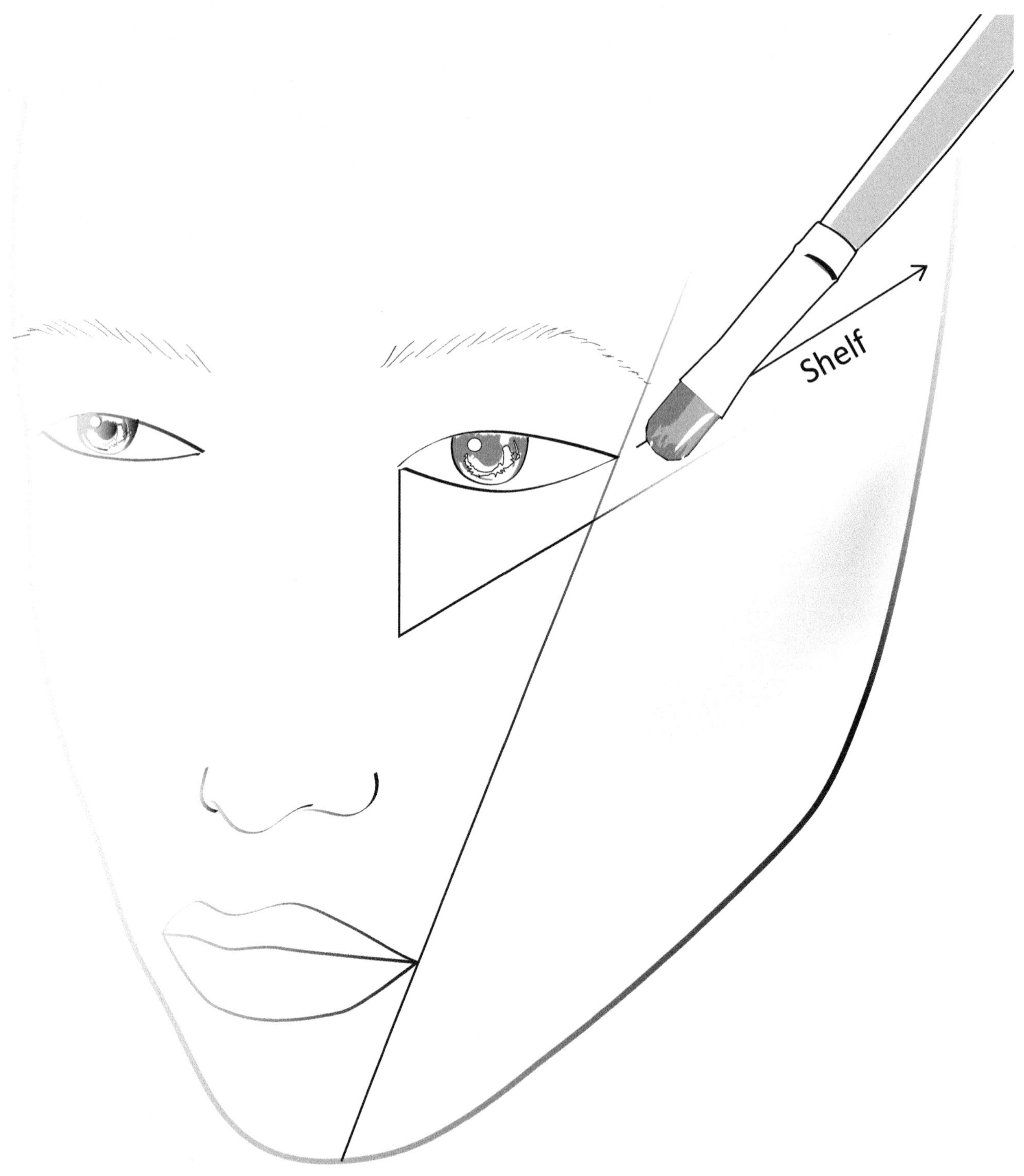

How:

- Apply highlighter along shelf of the cheekbone outside the heart line back towards the hairline
- Blend smoothly for glowing skin-like finish.

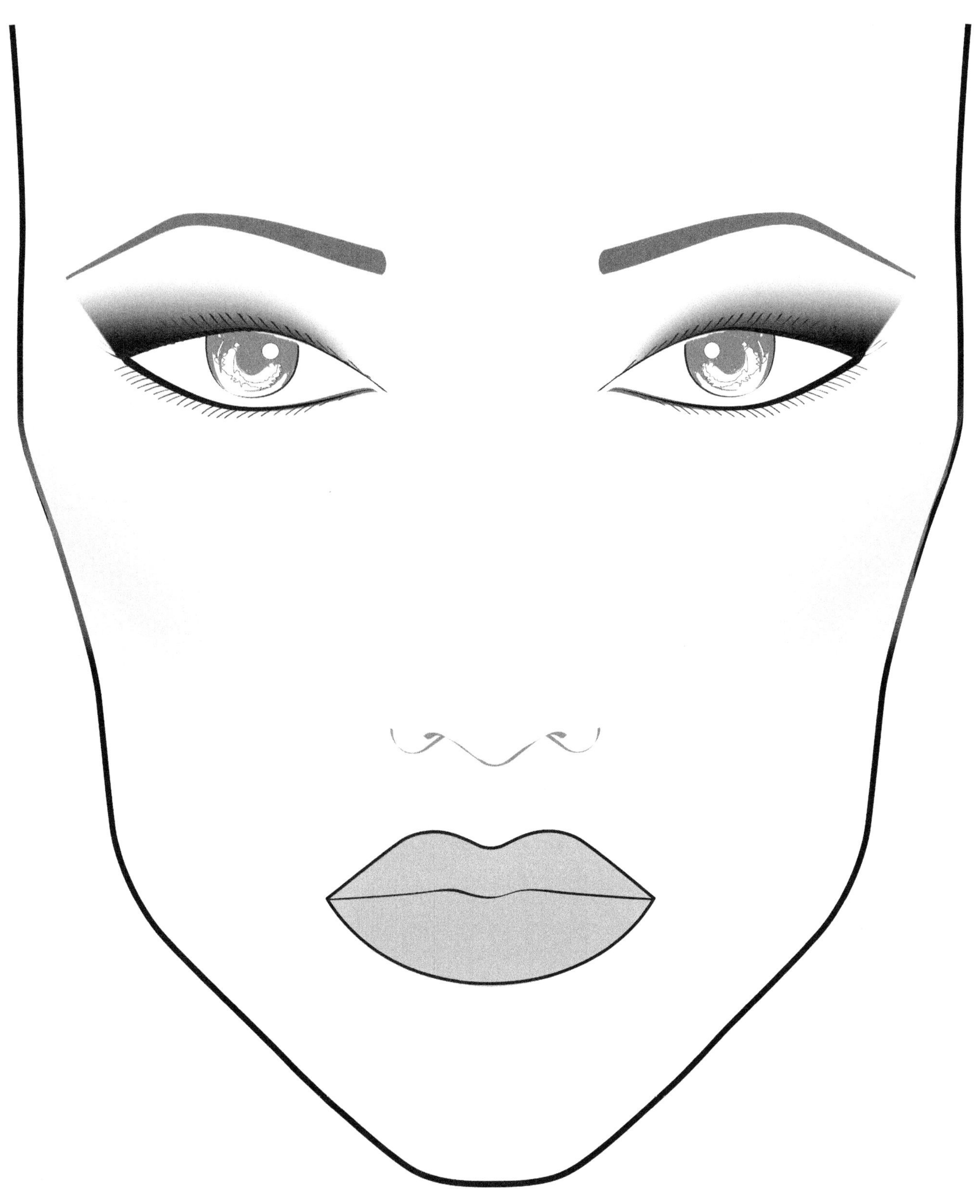

The main three elements of authentic beauty makeup; eyes-lips-cheeks are complete. Now for mascara.

Mascara

Why:

Mascara creates a healthier, shinier, thicker appearance to eye lashes while drawing focus more intently to the eyes.

Mascara is one of the main cosmetics worn by most cosmetics wearers. Mascara is brilliant in that it captures the very nature of the eye while enhancing it. Just as with lash liner where shape of the eye is highlighted by focusing on the lashes as the basis for our application, mascara takes that enhancement and runs it along every fiber of the eyelash.

As with all of the makeup, it is important to find the right balance of mascara with the rest of the beauty makeup look. Not enough, and the look lacks that extra sizzle which makes the eye the focal point of the makeup. Too much and the thought is 'why so much mascara' as the eyes are the place our gaze continually returns to on anyone's face.
The makeup artist must create the effect that fulfills the goal of the look.

Mascara is applied last because powder product tends to float around and stick to lashes which dull them. Whenever possible, apply the mascara last to create the shiniest, healthiest looking lashes possible. If more powder is needed to smooth and set the look, apply the finishing powder before mascara.

For mascara, return to the concept of the sweet spot of the eye. If mascara is applied evenly across all the lashes, we have a wall of lashes. If the mascara becomes increasingly thicker as it moves from the inner to the outer corner of the eye, the lashes build in volume and support the appearance of the eyes growing wider. The goal of mascara is to make the sweet spot of the eye, the area from the pupil of the eye out to the corner, grab more focus. Also attempt to make the outer lashes break outside the heart line to pull even more focus to the openness of the eyes. This technique is referred to as, 'Bambi the lash'.

Please note: It is suggested to apply a final smoothing application of translucent powder before the mascara so that powder doesn't stick to wet lashes and create a dull ashy lash instead of a glossy lash. A final powder will create an overall layer of smoothness to the skin and the contour/blush application, as well as further the wearing life of the foundation.

Step 1-
Upper lashes

Applying mascara to someone else requires giving specific instructions to the model.

- Ask the model to look at a specific spot on the ground. If they are just asked to look down, they will invariably look up as the mascara wand comes towards their eyes. If they are looking at a spot, they will stay focused on the spot.
- Take control of the eyelid by gently laying your thumb over the eyelid and gently lifting up to raise the lashes.
- Start with the outer lashes. Try to drag the outer lashes sideways and outwards with the mascara wand. This motion will change the direction that the outer eyelash hairs are going from forward to sideways.

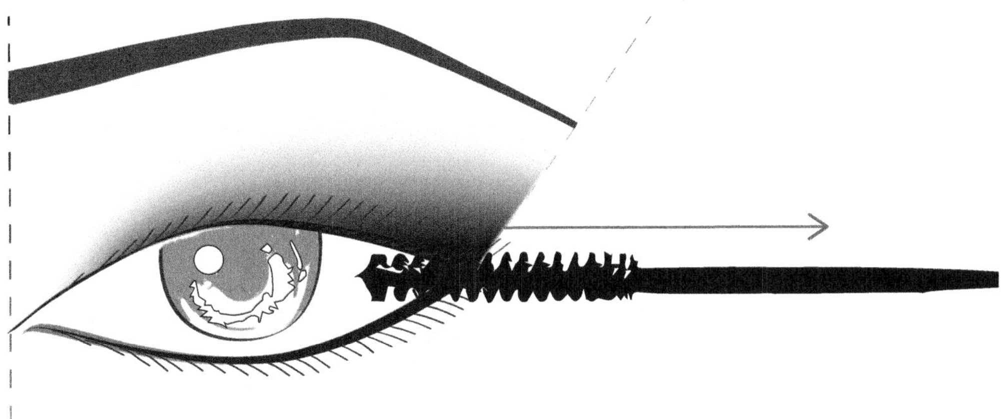

- Because the outer lashes need to be thicker, simply apply more mascara to the outer lashes and they will be thicker.
- The mascara will act as a gel so as it dries, it will hold the lashes in their new position.
- Next brush center lashes forward and upward. Wiggling the mascara wand back and forth at the base of the lashes before brushing away from the eye will create a thicker base of the lashes.

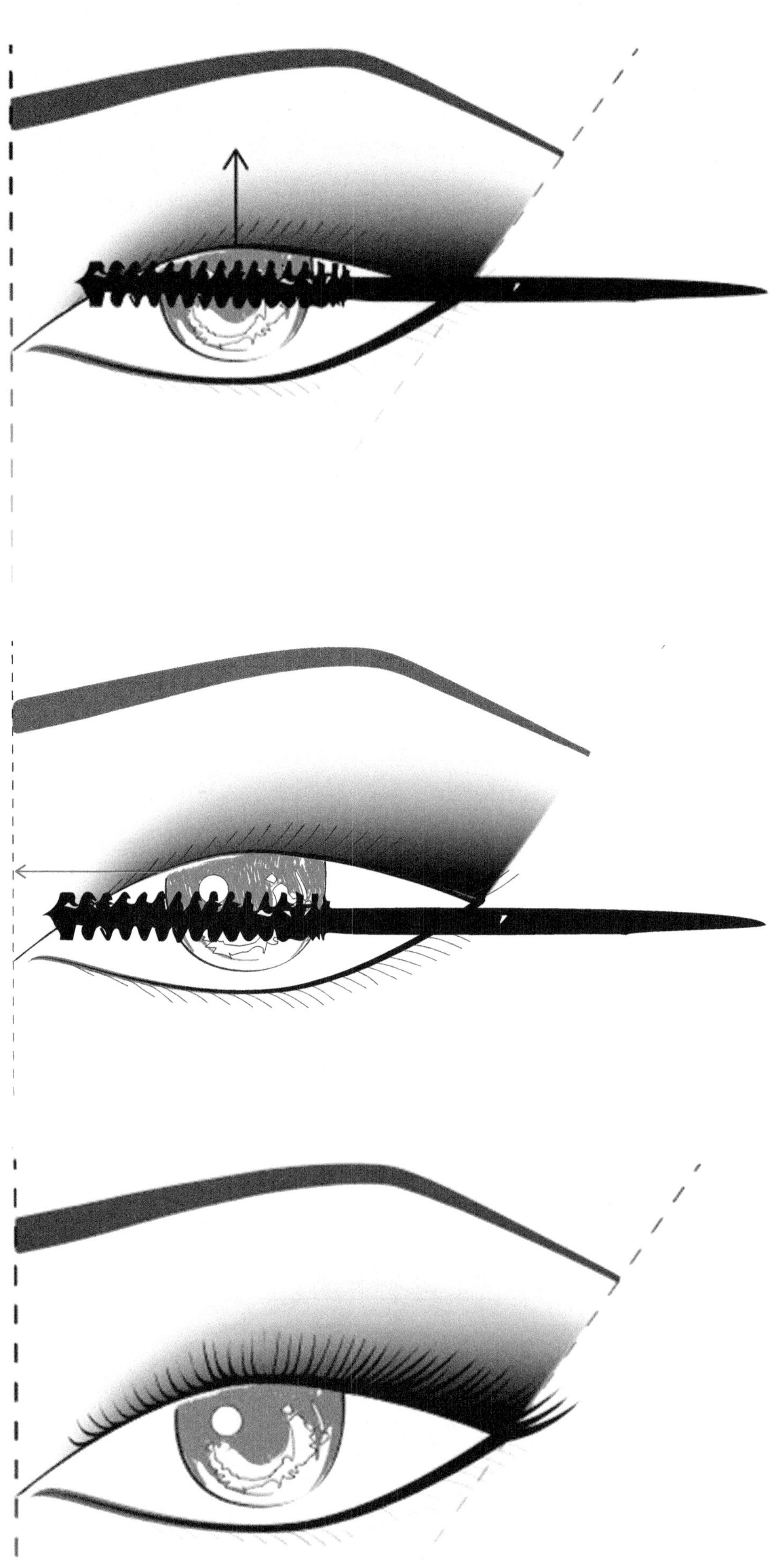

- Lastly, if possible, fan the inner lashes in towards the nose. This will increase the spread or fanning of the lashes to achieve the fullest looking lashes possible.

This is the desired appearance of the top lashes.

Step 2 - Lower lashes (optional)

Next, apply mascara to the bottom lashes (if using mascara on the bottom lashes).

- Use the tip of the mascara wand for bottom lashes.
- Ask the model to look up.
- Now sketch back and forth ('tickle') the bottom lashes with the tip of the mascara wand.
- This back and forth motion will give control over the intensity of the mascara on the bottom lashes.
- Make bottom lashes ½ the intensity of the top lashes.

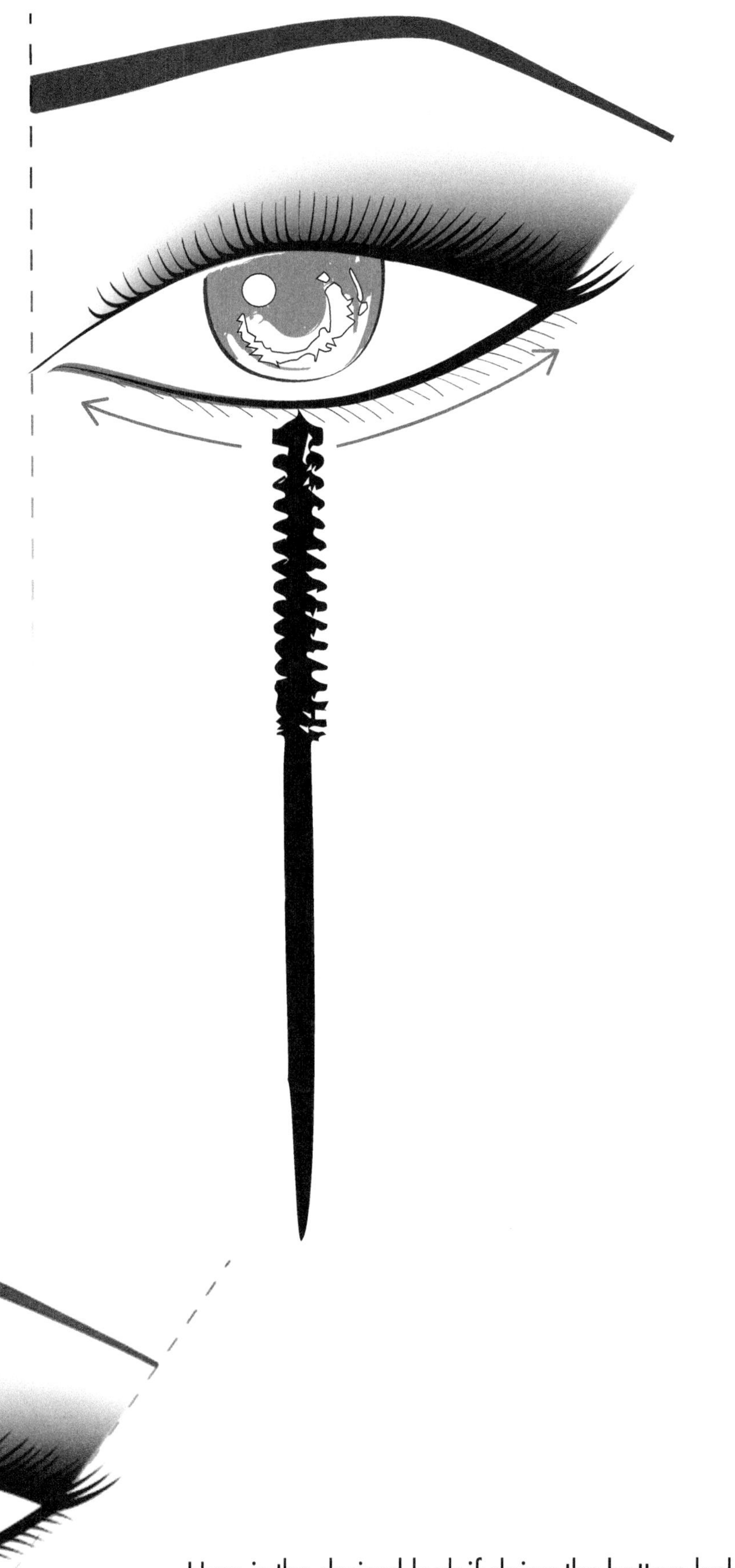

Here is the desired look if doing the bottom lashes.

Finish

Now that the makeup is complete, step back and assess the overall application. If doing makeup on yourself, look away from the mirror, move at least 3 feet back then look at your work. When doing someone else's makeup, also look away from the model, move back 3 feet and then look at the overall application.

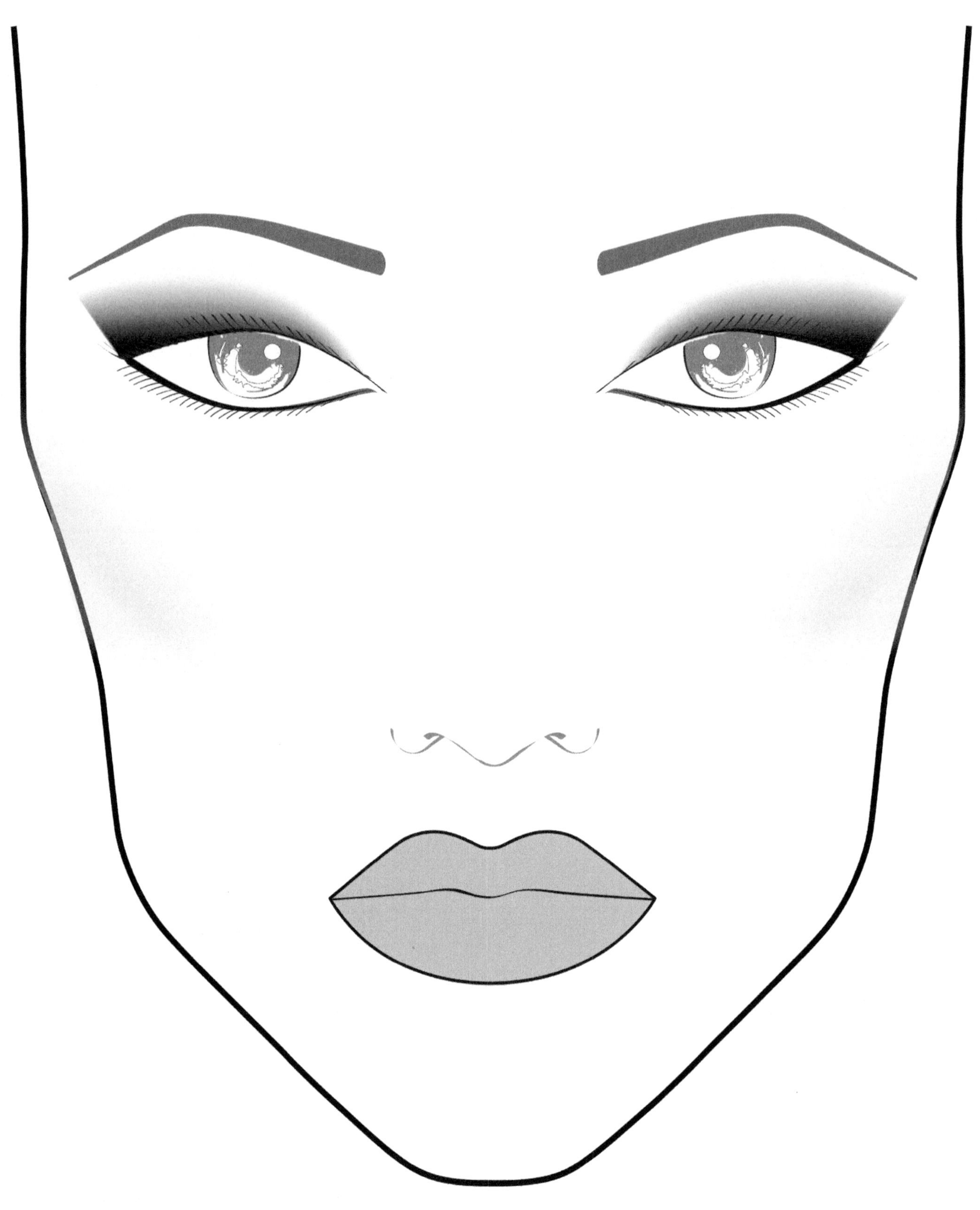

This gives a fresh perspective on the overall effect of the application. After an objective look at the final result, decide what, if anything, needs to be done to adjust the makeup for the desired look.

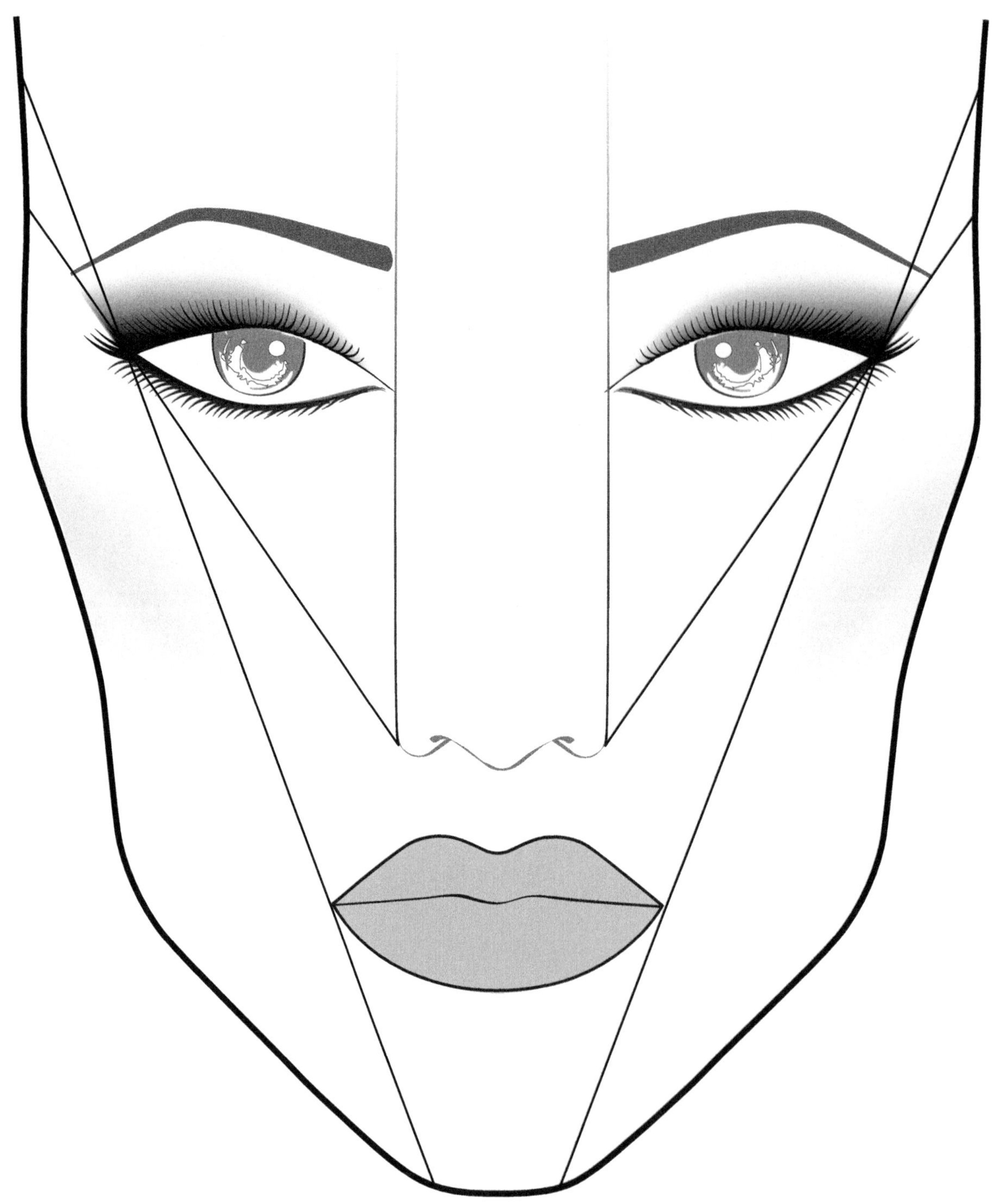

This manual is designed to provide everything needed to achieve a perfect authentic beauty makeup application. The *Face with a Heart* method provides the blueprint to apply anyone's makeup, including your own. Like any recipe, knowing where to start, where to end, and what to do in between eliminates guesswork and trial and error. This method adapts to any face and the result is always original because the approach is authentic.

My wish is for everyone to master their makeup application, be able to do it in a timely fashion, and feel authentically beautiful every day.

May every face be a
Face with a Heart

CPSIA information can be obtained
at www.ICGtesting.com
Printed in the USA
LVOW05s0551271115
464316LV00043B/229/P